MW00619902

RECIPES

FOR

LIFE!

10 Basic Principles of
Biblical Nutrition

Beth M. Ley, Ph.D.

BL Publications
Hanover, MN

BL Publications
Hanover, MN 55341

1-877-BOOKS11
www.blpublications.com
email: bley@blpublications.com

Library of Congress Cataloging-in-Publication Data

Ley, Beth M., 1964-

Printed in the United States of America

This book is not intended as medical advice. Its purpose is solely educational. Please consult your healthcare professional for all health problems.

YOU NEED TO KNOW...
THE HEALTH MESSAGE

Do you not know that you are God's temple and that God's Spirit dwells in you? If anyone destroys God's temple, God will destroy him, For God's temple is holy and that temple you are. *1 Corinthians 3:16-17*

So, whether you eat or drink, or whatever you do, do all to the glory of God. *1 Corinthians 10:31*

Table of Contents

Introduction 5

1. Eat Foods the Way God Made Them 7

2. Follow The Rules Given to Us in the Word 8

3. Eat and Drink in Moderation 10

4. Eat to Nourish Our Bodies, Not Only to Satisfy Flesh 12

5. Avoid Artificial, Man-made Chemicals and Additives 13

6. Eat Fresh Foods (without Preservatives, Freezing, etc.) as . .
   Much as Possible. 15

7. Consume Wild, Free-range, Drug-free Meats and Organic . .
   Dairy Products as Much as Possible 17

8. Consume Non-GMO or GE Foods (Genetically Modified . . . .
   Organisms or Genetically Engineered) 19

9. Focus on "In Season" Foods and Those Native to Your . . . . .
   Growing Area 23

10. Know WHO Your Healer is! 24

Commonly Asked Q & A's 26

Simple Tips For Eating Out 40

Quality Whole Foods For Life 45

Cooking Whole Foods From Scratch 57

Tips on Resources 59

Healthy Alternatives 60

What's Cooking in Beth's Kitchen 67

Recipe Index **68-71**

Glycemic Index 224

About the Author 229

Books from BL Publications 230

Order Form 232

Dedication

I am dedicating this 2nd edition of "Recipes For Life" to my parents who made this printing possible.

I especially thank my mother who had me in the kitchen cooking at a very young age and who did not ever "correct" me for not following the recipe exactly. I learned as a young age that kitchens were a wonderful creative outlet.

INTRODUCTION

The revelation that God cares about our eating habits is new to many even though the Bible tells us what foods man was supposed to eat right after it tells us about the creation of man. Genesis 1:12 says, *And the earth brought forth grass, and herb yielding seed after his kind, and the tree yielding fruit, whose seed was in itself, after his kind: and God saw that it was good. A* few verses later God said, *See, I have given you every herb that yields seed which is on the face of all the earth, and every tree whose fruit yields seed; to you it shall be for food.* (Genesis 1:29)

As the creation of God, we have a God-given responsibility to take care of our bodies by consuming the foods that God has provided for us.

Psalms 139 tells us that we are fearfully and wonderfully made. Our bodies are designed to heal themselves. The medical community call this the immune system. To have an optimal functioning immune system and optimal health, we simply need to feed the body the nutrients it needs to continue in it's continual state of healing and repair. Just like we need to feed our cars the right kind of fuel to run correctly, we need to give our bodies the right kind of fuel.

Living a godly, pure life is how God desires us to live. This He can bless! *Be not wise in thine own eyes: fear the LORD, and depart from evil. It shall be health to thy navel, and marrow to thy bones.* Proverbs 3:7-8

This book, *Recipes for Life!* outlines the basic principals for healthy eating and then provides instruction on how to buy, prepare and cook healthy foods.

You may notice that unlike some recipe books, I have chosen not to include specific nutritional data for each recipe containing information like calories, fat grams, or sugar, fat and protein exchanges. I personally do not place much emphasis on these concepts which I consider to be predominantly man's ideas involving the food pyramid and other man-made ideas to eating. I am personally not impressed with the success of these "programs" and instead choose to promote what I know works; What I call "Biblical Nutrition," concepts which simply promote healthy, natural whole foods, and returning to the traditional diets of our ancestors. Through these simple concepts I have personally seen men and women lose up to 100 pounds, get off their medications for high blood sugar, high blood pressure, elevated cholesterol and many, many others restoring their health and joy in life!

I believe it is inappropriate to set rules as to how many calories or fat grams a person should eat because it varies too greatly according to a person's lifestyle (how physically active they are), their genetics (the diet their ancestors ate for the last few hundred or thousand of years), their present state of health, the climate they live in, etc. I prefer the simple rules outlined in this book. These principals promote good health and life! They work!

So choose to eat well and live!

1. Eat Food the Way God Made It as Much as Possible

Genesis 1:12 tells us that ALL the foods that He created for us were good. They were perfect, containing everything that we need to sustain and nourish our bodies. When man adds or subtracts anything from the way God designed it, there is compromise. The more processing a food undergoes, the more compromise and the more risk for development of health problems.

After the flood, God preserved all clean animals (as most vegetation was destroyed in the food) for us to eat and said in Genesis 9:3-4; *Every living thing that lives shall be meat for you, even as the green herb have I given you all things. But the flesh with the life thereof, which is the blood thereof, shall ye not eat.*

Note: I am not talking about eating all food raw. I am talking about avoiding commercially processed and man-made foods (such as soda pop, margarine, white flour and sugar and things containing them, processed meats, processed dairy products, etc.)

2. Follow The Rules Given to us in the Word

Many people do not think about the fact that the first sin involved food. Adam and Eve are instructed and warned that eating improperly will cost them their lives: And the LORD God commanded the man, saying, "*Of every tree of the garden you may freely eat; but of the tree of the knowledge of good and evil you shall not eat, for in the day that you eat of it you shall surely die.* (Genesis 2:16-17)

God has ordained a perfect eating plan for us. When followed, it will give us health, vitality, strength, long life, and. . . even wisdom. (Read Daniel Chapter1) Secondly, eating the wrong foods can lead to unnecessary illnesses and even a premature death.

The dietary laws given to us in Leviticus 11 still apply to us today. Here God defines which animal foods are fit for us to eat and calls them clean and which are unfit for us to eat, and calls them unclean. Many people are confused by the dream in which Peter had (Acts 10:9) of the animals in a sheet where he heard God say, *Kill and eat.* Peter objects and says, not so Lord, for I have never eaten anything that is unclean or common. God says *"what Yahweh has cleansed, that shall not call common."* In reality, God was **not** saying that these foods were now clean (note there were no sea animals in the sheet.)

When God gives a dream or vision, it rarely, IF EVER, has a literal meaning, but instead, a spiritual interpretation is required. The things in the dream represent something else.

Just as Jesus spoke in parables, so are our dreams and visions, which require interpretation.

The cleansing God was referring to was the cleansing of the Gentiles (through Christ's death our sins are cleansed). At that time the Jews and the Gentiles were not allowed to associate together, and especially eat together. The Jewish leaders proposed a large number of additional rules about things that were not actually according to God's plan, God was trying to show Peter this. Peter was hungry, knowing they were about to eat soon, but probably very nervous about eating with the Gentiles (for the first time) that he was visiting.

In the new testament, there are many examples where unclean foods are discussed, such as: *Wherefore come out from among them, and be ye separate, saith the Lord, and touch not the unclean thing; and I will receive you*, (Amplified says, *treat you with favor*), *Having therefore these promises, dearly beloved, let us cleanse ourselves from all filthiness of the flesh and spirit, perfecting holiness in the fear of God.* 2 Chronicles 6:17 and 7:1

If it were true that the foods which God had deemed unclean *were* clean, how could so many references to the unclean be applicable? It is because God does not change His mind. (Hebrews 6:17) If He says something is unclean, it stays unclean. Because of the blood that was shed for us thankfully, we are no longer UNDER the law and it is not a sin if we do eat something that is unclean.

All things are lawful unto me, but all things are not expedient (beneficial): all things are lawful for me, but I will not be brought under the power of any. Meats for the belly, and the belly for meats: but God shall destroy both it and them. (1 Corinthians 6:12-13)

3. Eat and Drink in Moderation

There are many scriptures that warn us of the sins of gluttony and drunkenness (Proverbs 23:20-21, 25:16). Temperance (moderation) is one of the fruits of the spirit which we should all abide in in all we do.

Most people in affluent societies eat and drink too much. Scientific evidence has proven that overweight increases mortality from diabetes, digestive diseases, and coronary disease. Most authorities agree that overeating and underactivity cause 95% of obesity.

Here is an interesting perspective on eating foods the way God made them vs. processed foods. *And the LORD God commanded the man, saying, Of every tree of the garden thou may **freely eat**.* (Genesis 2:16)

Whole natural foods fill you up and satisfy you, whereas processed foods you can eat and eat and still crave more! Many people eat until their stomach hurts (which causes it to expand making room for more food and calories), yet the basic nutritional needs are not met. The result is that today we are a society of undernourished, but overweight people. It is estimated that 65% of the population today in the US is overweight.

When fiber is removed (through processing) foods are much less filling and we tend to eat more, which means more calories and more weight! It is easy to see how Satan continues to use food (just like the first sin) to get us to sin today.

The original vegetarian diet that God recommended would be high in complex carbohydrates, high in fiber, fairly low in protein, low in saturated fat, low in sodium. This diet featured **grains, beans, legumes, nuts, seeds, vegetables, fruit, herbs** and **spices.**

Natural foods fill us up and satisfy us...

Man-made foods simply appeal to our taste buds...

so we eat and eat...

never getting satisfied!

4. Eat to Nourish the Body, Not only to Satisfy the Flesh

We should be eating to supply our bodies the nutrients it needs (to live) rather than living to eat. 1 Corinthians 10:31 tells us *"in all things, in what you eat and drink do all to the glory of God. "*

Our food choices should not be to feed our fleshly desires (based on taste only). Does eating Krispy Kreme donuts glorify God or does it glorify our flesh? These processed foods which are far more "man-made" than natural simply do not support the bodies nutritional needs (providing life) but rather please the flesh and ROB the body of nutrients and therefore, create deficiencies, health problems and death.

One very important thing I believe God had to teach me was to not eat if I wasn't hungry. If our body is not actually craving food... then it may be really easy to be feeding the flesh - or our taste buds.

5. Avoid Artificial, Man-made Chemicals and Additives

There are a lot of foods which are actually "fake" (counterfeits of the real thing). Many of them taste good, even very good. This is how they are designed, but they provide no nutritional value whatsoever and many of them are highly detrimental to our health. One example is margarine and hydrogenated oil products, which I call fake fats. These are highly processed vegetable oil products designed to be a cholesterol-free butter alternative.

These are very high in trans fatty acids, a known carcinogen of which there is no "safe" level of consumption, which actually increases blood cholesterol and triglyceride levels to a greater extent than eating butter (which is natural).

Look at the ingredients found in a Burger King strawberry milk shake: amylacetate, amyl butyrate, amyl valerate, anethol, anisyl formate, benzyl acetate, benzyl isobutyrate, butyric acid, cinnamyl isobutyrate, cinnamyl valerate, cognac essential oil, diacetyl, dipropyl ketone, ethyl acetate, ethyl amyl ketone, ethyl butyrate, ethyl cinnamate, ethyl heptanoate, ethyl heptylate, ethlyl lactate, ethyl methylphenylglycidate, ethyl nitrate, ethyl propionate, ethyl valerate, heliotropin, hydroxyphenyl-2-butonone (10% solution in alcohol), a-ionone, isobutyl anthranilate, isobutyl butyrate, lemon essential oil, maltol, 4-methylactophenone, methyl anthranilate, methyl benzoate, methyl cinnamate, methyl heptine carbonate, methyl naphthyl ketone, methyl salicylate, mint essential oil, neroli essential oil, nerolin, neryl isobutyrate, orris butter, phenethyl alcohol, rose, rum ether, g-undecalactone, vanillin and solvent.

Funny, I thought a strawberry milk shake contained strawberries, milk and ice cream. (which I am NOT saying is a healthy food choice. BUT, if you make your own (including homemade ice cream) it is whole lot healthier than the above listed chemicals!)

Read the labels on your foods and you would probably be very surprised at all the man-made chemicals added. Many of them are NOT safe, contrary to what many believe. For example, the common thickening agent, carrageenin, which comes from red seaweed, can cause ulcerations and cancer of the gastrointestinal tract and possibly the breast. (Tobacman)

It is often added to salad dressing, soy and rice milk, yogurt (especially the fruit-flavored kinds), ice cream, cottage cheese and other processed foods.

Another commonly added chemical is aspartame. This substance can be found in almost any "diet" or reduced calorie item Aspartame receives the most health complaints by the FDA, associated with migraine headaches, nerve damage, MS-related symptoms, and about 75 other health complaints.

6. Eat Fresh Foods (without Preservative, Freezing, etc.) as Much as Possible

Every living thing that lives shall be meat for you, even as the green herb have I given you all things - but the flesh with the life thereof, which is the blood thereof, shall ye not eat. (Genesis 9:3)

Living foods are perishable. The foods that God gave us to eat are all perishable, even if you refrigerate them, they have a relatively short shelf life.

I do not believe that God intended us to eat all of our foods raw. I do not believe He has a problem with cooking at all. All the sacrificial animals and grains were "cooked" on a fire. The point is that even cooked foods which are prepared in our own kitchens are perishable, they have a relatively short shelf life, even if kept in the refrigerator.

Manna was given to the people on a daily basis (except on the Sabbath). We were taught to ask for our "daily bread." (Matthew 6:11) Bread made with freshly ground grains, is only fresh for about 1-2 days.

Today's processed breads may have a expiration date of weeks or months after it's production. Many processed crackers and baked goods have expiration dates several years past production. This is done for commercial gain, not in the interest of our health. Many nutrients which would have gone rancid are removed to extend shelf life... the result of this is compromise to our health.

Never consume processed meat products such as pepperoni, hot dogs, luncheon meats, etc. Preserved meats are not fresh, which is the way God tells us to eat our foods. These contain nitrates, which are carcinogenic (cause cancer), and other Preservative. Processed meat products also contain trans-fatty acids which are known to contribute to high blood sugar and increase risk for development of Type II diabetes.

Saturated fats and cholesterol (naturally found in meat and dairy products) are not as harmful as they were once thought to be as long as these are not consumed excessively. Trans-fatty acids found in processed meats, refined vegetable oils, such as margarine and shortening are the real culprits to destroying our health. AVOID all fried foods, they are all high in trans fatty acids!

7. Consume Wild, Free-range, Drug-free Meats and Organic and Raw Dairy Products as Much as Possible

After the flood, God allowed us to eat clean meats. *Every moving thing that lives shall be food for you. I have given you all things, even as the green herbs.* (Genesis 9:3)

Noah preserved seven pairs of all clean animals (as most vegetation was destroyed in the food) to eat and for sacrifice. (Genesis 9:3-4) God instructed Noah to bring only two of the unclean animals aboard the arch.

The problem today is that the meat we consume is a far cry different than the animals at that time. Industrialized farming practices, hormones, antibiotics, unclean and unnatural feed used today has greatly disrupted God's plan and the quality of meat available to us.

Look for fresh (preferably never frozen), wild, clean fish (or catch your own) and meat from grass-fed cows, sheep, goats, clean game animals and grain-fed poultry (also called free-range).

Look for Kosher meats where the animals are killed according to Levitical law. This is a more humane way prevents huge amounts of unhealthy (stress) hormones from getting released into the blood and meat that God never intended. (This is what happens in today's slaughter houses.) Also remember, the bible strictly tells us never to consume the blood. (Acts 15:20)

Hormones in meat products create hormonal imbalances in humans who consume them, leading to weight gain, fertility problems, endocrine disorders, possibly cancer, and much more.

Antibiotics given to animals are known to result in mutated, antibiotic-resistant strains of bacteria (such as E-coli) that can be deadly if consumed.

Eat food grown in good soil organically. Try to obtain or grow your own high-quality food. Luke 13:6-9, Proverbs 28:19, Deuteronomy 14:22-23, and many other statutes of the Biblical laws are based on God's ideal, agricultural, society. In today's industrial age, it is difficult to get into harmony with God's ways, but we ought to do the best we can by making an effort either by growing what we can on our own or by looking for organically- grown foods in the market place.

Inorganic chemical fertilizers and pesticides are know to kill the healthy, necessary probiotics in the soil which interferes with the plants absorption of minerals from the soil. It not only harms the soil, but reduces the nutritional value of the food grown there.

Look for organic and Kosher products.

8. Consume Non-GMO or GE Foods (Genetically Modified Organisms or Genetically Engineered)

There is no question that God strongly disapproves of genetically modified foods, which is defined as altering the genetic blueprint of something by artificially transplanting some of the genetic material from another organism, including humans and other animals. This is done to (supposedly) increase resistance to frost, infection and disease, shelf life, production yield or for some other commercially prosperous reason.

A few examples include splicing a gene from jelly fish into potatoes, spider genes into goats, flounder (fish) genes into tomatoes. This is not a joke - they are actually putting fish genes in our tomatoes to make them more resistant to frost. If God would have wanted fish genes in our tomatoes, He would have put them there Himself! Why do people think they can do a better job of creating than He did? No wonder store tomatoes taste so bad!

The three largest crops in the US containing GMOs are corn (35-50%), soybeans (55-65%) and cotton (50-60%). These products and their by-products are in thousands upon thousands of products, many which we unknowingly consume everyday. Don't forget, for example, corn syrup, corn starch, corn flour, corn meal, corn oil and maltodextrin are all from corn! Read your labels! Products which are GMO-free will state it on the label - otherwise, we really don't even know what we are eating any more!

Genesis 1:11-12 tells us that *the earth brought forth grass and herb yielding seed after his kind, and the tree yielding fruit, whose seed was in itself, after his kind; and God saw that it was good.* Apparently, scientists (and marketers) don't think that God did a good enough job when He created everything, and that they can do a better job. To me this is mocking God.

In Leviticus 19:19, God warns, *Thou shalt not let they cattle gender with a diverse kind; thou shalt not now they field with mingled seed; neither shall a garment mingled of linen and woolen come upon thee.* The same thing is stated in Deuteronomy 22:9-11. What they are doing today in these high biotech labs is far worse. We would do good to avoid them and not support what they are doing as it is clearly against the will of God!

For more information on this subject, please read *GMO's, Beware of the Coming Food Apocalypse, They're Playing God and Showing it Down your Throat!* by Greg Ciola, Axion Publishers.

From the book, *GMOs – Beware of the Food Apocalypse,* Through GMO foods, *"scientists are essentially mocking God by declaring that nearly everything He made is defective and can be improved upon and made better by them."*

In this book, Ciola explains what the world's interests are in GMOs, mostly financial, of course! They claim through plant and animal gene splicing they can do and are doing things like extending shelf life of produce, make them grow faster (combining human genes with tomatoes and peppers), reduce susceptibility to bacteria (combining a chicken gene with potatoes), increase quality of meat (adding human genes to chicken). The list goes on and on.

I like how Ciola put it. *"If God wanted a chicken gene in a potato, He would have created it that way in the first place. God is the master architect of all creation!"* Man needs to quit playing God!

Currently, only organic foods are the only products required to be grown free of GMOs. So aside from food you grow on your own and purchasing exclusively organic foods (which is more expensive), who knows what we are eating.

What we eat is very important to God. Don't forget the fall of man was due to man eating the forbidden fruit in the Garden of Eden.

For more information on Genetically Modified Organisms, read
GMOs - Beware of the Food Apocalypse by Greg Ciola.
Axion Publishers, 2001, 1-407-472-0120

For a good (healthy) tree bringeth not forth corrupt fruit; neither doth a corrupt tree bring forth good fruit. For every tree is known by his own fruit. For of thorns men do not gather figs, nor of a bramblebush gather they grapes. **Luke 6:43-44**

*Therefore they shall come and sing in the height of Zion, and shall flow together to the goodness of the LORD, for wheat, and for wine, and for oil, and for the young of the flock and of the herd: and **their soul shall be as a watered garden**; and they shall not sorrow any more at all.* **Jeremiah 31:12**

A watered garden produces fruit. Matthew 7: 17-20 states that we will know them by their fruit as every good tree bears good fruit, but a bad tree bears bad fruit. *The fruit of the spirit is love, joy, peace, patience, kindness, goodness, faithfulness, gentleness and self control.* **Galatians 5:22**

A healthy garden has no weeds (of sin) as they have been uprooted and removed. Weeds steal nutrients from the soil that interferes with the full potential development and yield of the garden. A healthy garden is well cared for and given the proper amounts of sunlight and water.

And the LORD shall guide thee continually, and satisfy thy soul in drought, and make fat thy bones: and thou shalt be like a watered garden, and like a spring of water, whose waters fail not. **Isaiah 58:11**

But while men slept, his enemy came and sowed tares among the wheat, and went his way. But when the blade was sprung up, and brought forth fruit, then appeared the tares also. So the servants of the householder came and said unto him, Sir, did not thou sow good seed in thy field? from whence then hath it tares? He said unto them, An enemy hath done this. The servants said unto him, Wilt thou then that we go and gather them up? But he said, Nay; lest while ye gather up the tares, ye root up also the wheat with them. Let both grow together until the harvest: and in the time of harvest I will say to the reapers, Gather ye together first the tares, and bind them in bundles to burn them: but gather the wheat into my barn. **Matthew 13:25-30**

9. Focus on "In Season" Foods and Those Native to Your Growing Area

Don't waste a lot of time and money importing foods that cannot be found in your region. If God would have thought that coconut oil should be a staple to the people in the midwest and Canada, he would have put palm trees there, and had the weather for them to grow. It's not that the food grown on the other side of the world to where you live have no value, it's that they have more value to the people living where it is grown.

Focus on locally-grown foods like honey, fish, meats, grains, vegetables, fruits, berries, etc. This does not mean that we can never enjoy the awesome variety of the foods of the world, but because are not genetically predisposed to process them in the body, if we eat an excess amount of those foods, we may develop sensitives to them.

It is easy for us to forget that things like mass transportation and refrigeration have only been available for the last half century or so. Interestingly, many of the diseases common in the industrialized world (cancer, heart disease, diabetes, even dental problems, etc.) were unheard of in areas where they still lived on unprocessed native foods.

10. KNOW Who Your Healer Is!

Jesus is Jehovah Raffia, the Healer, the Great Physician. Even if the doctors can't figure out what is wrong with you... Jesus knows. He knows your every ache and pain, every disappointment and every broken heart. This is what He died for.

Ask the Lord to heal you if you become sick, James 5:14-15. The world's way is to rely upon pharmaceuticals and doctors. God can certainly use these things, but they should not be the first place you look for help. Your faith in the power of God, and His promises to heal you, is what makes you whole. (Matthew 9:20-22)

Be joyful. This can only be done by producing the fruits of the Holy Spirit, Galatians 5:22-23, living by every word of the Eternal, Matthew 4:4. See also Proverbs 17:22, 14:30, 4:20-22.

Forgive! Lack of forgiveness is the number one reason that people do not receive their healing! The word tells us that

> *But He was wounded for our transgressions,*
> *He was bruised for our iniquities:*
> *the chastisement of our peace was upon him;*
> *and with his stripes we are healed.* Isaiah 53:5

bitterness (which stems from unforgiveness) is rottenest to the bones! (Proverbs 14:30)

Be active. This means keeping active with a lot of physical activity. This includes work (at your job or around the house, cleaning, chores, gardening, yard work, etc.), and also exercise and sports for enjoyment. (Proverbs 6:6-11, 10:4-5, 12:11, 20:13, 14:23 and Timothy 4:7-8.)

Obtain proper sleep and rest. Exodus 20:8-11 is a health law as well as a spiritual law. He gives His beloved sleep (Psalms 4:8, 127:1-2, Ecclesiastes 5:12.)

Keep your body clean (holiness) and fast occasionally for both spiritual and physical health. Isaiah 52:11, II Corinthians 7:1, and I John 3:3 refer both to physical and spiritual cleanliness. Fasting is a way to cleanse your body internally, Isaiah 58:6-8.

Depart ye, depart ye, go ye out from thence, touch no unclean thing; go ye out of the midst of her; be ye clean, that bear the vessels of the LORD. Isaiah 52:11

Having therefore these promises, dearly beloved, let us cleanse ourselves from all filthiness of the flesh and spirit, perfecting holiness in the fear of God.
2 Corinthians 7:1

COMMONLY ASKED Q'S & A'S

Q: Is it "Biblical" to take supplements?

A: This a question you probably need to ask God yourself. When I asked Him, He told me that the land and water were toxic and that they were not the same (as far as mineral content, etc.) as they were even 100 years ago (due to abuse and use of pesticides and inorganic fertilizers, etc.). Therefore, supplements were basically a wise thing to take. If you do not have peace about taking them and feel God is directing you not to take them, then you should be obedient.

The word does tell us that *"the leaves of the trees shall be for the healing of nations"* (Rev. 22:2). While this can be interpreted prophetically for the end times, it can also be interpreted in the natural. We know that many leaves of trees (such as the leaves of the Ginkgo Biloba tree) have incredible therapeutic properties that can be used preventatively and also therapeutically. Research on Ginkgo biloba has identified its many beneficial properties. It is a powerful antioxidant which protects us from depressed antioxidant levels and stress. (White) Ginkgo also plays a role in enhancing or protecting memory and other brain functions.

Ginkgo is also important for the inhibition of PAF (platelet aggregation factor). This is associated with platelet clotting, allergic reactions and acute inflammation. Too much PAF can also inhibit proper functioning of the cardiovascular system. (Pietri, Maitra)

Numerous studies show that ginkgo biloba extract helps us to maintain adequate antioxidant nutrition for our brain to function, such as remembering where you put your keys or glasses, what you were supposed to pick up at the grocery store or the directions to a place you haven't been in a few months. (Stoll, Grassel)

Figs contain Benzaldehyde, which provides antitumor activity. In one study with 65 patients with inoperable cancer in the advanced stages given Benzaldehyde 55% responded favorably; seven patients achieved complete recovery, 29 achieved partial improvement, 24 remained stable, and only five showed progression of the disease. (Kochi) In the Old Testament, Isaiah called for figs to heal King Hezekiah who was "sick unto death" from "a boil," which was probably cancer. The king recovered.

Figs also contain antibacterial, antiparasitic enzymes called ficins that aid digestion.

Garlic and Onions have lipid lowering and anti-clotting properties which protect us against heart disease and also contain sulfides that seem to protect against stomach cancer. They stimulate enzymes within cells which detoxify cancer-causing chemicals.

Numerous research groups have demonstrated garlic's ability to significantly decrease LDL cholesterol and triglyceride, inhibit platelet aggregation (help prevent blood clots), inhibit proliferative (plaque promoting) activity, enhance vascular permeability, and provide antioxidant protection. Garlic compounds also stimulate the formation of glutathione an amino acid that detoxifies foreign chemicals and is a powerful antioxidant.

There are many, many foods with specific chemicals with

incredible healing properties. In my book, **Phytonutrients, Medicinal Nutrients Found in Nature**, I discuss many of them.

Q: What about milk?

A: Milk (and honey) are referred to over 20 times in the Bible, referring to God's promise to the Israelites, *to give thee, a land flowing with milk and honey* (Exd. 13:5, Deut. 27:3, etc.). This is referring to a land rich in vegetation which would be plentiful and provide for their needs.

Milk was not normally often consumed by adults in Biblical times. Because they had no refrigeration, milk would quickly go sour. Fresh goats milk would be more likely to be consumed than cow's milk. However, it was more likely that they used it to make cheese (curds), yogurt or other cultured items.

Children were given breast milk, if not from their mother, a wet nurse, until they were naturally weaned around three or four years old. After that, they were old enough to eat the foods the rest of the family was eating.

The problem with milk today is the pasteurization and homogenization processes it goes through greatly changes it from the way that God originally designed it. These procedures greatly inhibits our ability to absorb the calcium it does contain. Deceptive marketing by the dairy industry leads us to believe that milk is a good source of calcium. While it does contain calcium, it is not very absorbable (the low magnesium content is another reason). In fact, a serving of cooked broccoli contains more absorbable calcium than a glass of milk or serving of cheese does.

For more information on this subject, I suggest reading, "*How to Fight Osteoporosis and Win*" or "*Calcium: The Facts*." For more information on the benefits of breast feeding and colostrum, read "*Colostrum: Nature's Gift to the Immune System*."

Q: Isn't sugar natural? What about brown sugar?

A: Sugar is highly processed and refined and is a far cry from it's original source of sugar cane or sugar beets. Over 90% of the nutrients are lost, including all the fiber, making it actually far more of a detriment to our health than to serve of any benefit (unless someone is in a diabetic coma from an overdose of insulin where their blood sugar has dropped to a dangerously low level.)

All carbohydrate (sugar is a simple carbohydrate) consumption **requires** the B-vitamins, minerals, etc. that God put in the original sugar cane or sugar beets, for digestion in the body. When those nutrients are stripped out, we actually end up creating deficiencies of all those nutrients when we consume sugar. Over time this leads to weight gain, obesity, diabetes, elevated triglycerides, heart disease, immune suppression and many other health problems.

Brown sugar is simply highly processed white sugar sprayed with some molasses. Molasses is actually a by-product of the refining process and does contain some minerals such as iron, chromium, but is a far cry from God's original plan. God gave us honey, maple syrup and stevia (a plant with very sweet tasting leaves) to use as natural sweeteners. He does warn us, however, in Proverb 25:27, *It is not good to*

29

eat much honey: so for men to search their own glory is not glory. God reminds us not to eat (honey or anything else) to satisfy our own fleshly desires.

For more information on sweeteners, I suggest reading "*How Did We Get So Fat?*" and "*Diabetes to Wholeness.*"

If you find honey, eat just enough; too much of it, and you will vomit. Proverbs 25:16

Q: What about coffee?

A: Coffee beans come from a plant. God certainly gave us the approval to eat plant foods so I see no reason to ban it from our diet. However, because of it's caffeine content and it's strong acidic effect on the body, I do put it the same category as honey and butter. We need to be careful not to consume too much. Caffeine can be addicting, so I do NOT encourage DAILY coffee consumption and when you do, I suggesting limiting your intake to two cups. Studies now show that OVER 4 cups daily MAY contribute to elevated cholesterol and can aggravate hypertension in individuals prone to high blood pressure.

I do NOT recommend decaffeinated coffee for two reasons. First, God created it with caffeine so I feel that is how we should consume it. Second, the chemical solvents used in the decaffeination process are likely to be more harmful than the caffeine.

If you are a coffee drinker, I encourage you to drink organically-grown coffee. I encourage you to not drink coffee every day. There are many delicious herbal teas and other beverages you can enjoy instead.

Q: Does God really want us to deprive ourselves of all the good tasting foods that are available to us?

A: God designed our bodies in an incredible way. It actually heals itself. We don't have to do a thing... except feed it the nutrients it requires to maintain the integrity of God's plan. This is not hard. He told us, right after he created us, what we need to eat. Eat the foods that He made. These are the foods that will maintain our health. These other (man-made and man-altered foods) tear down our health rather than build it up.

The world may have convinced you that you have no time to garden, shop or cook, but this (fast-food lifestyle) is the way of the world, not God. It is easy to see the effects. Two-third of the U.S. population is over-weight (no doubt, from consuming too many refined, empty-calorie, good tasting, convenient foods.

Think about how many servings of potato chips you can eat verses how many servings of fresh raw vegetables, or how many baked potatoes? Refined foods lack fiber and nutrients that will satisfy our cravings and hunger. Real food fills us up!

Q: What is so bad about eating processed food?

A: The four main nutritional areas we are depleted in due to eating a processed diet are:

1. **Fiber**
2. **Omega-3 Fatty Acids**
3. **Minerals**
4. **Antioxidants and Phytochemicals**

Deficiencies of these crucial nutrients contribute to or cause the major health problems seen today! Diabetes, heart disease, high blood pressure, constipation, obesity, etc. This means that these health problems are treatable, reversible and preventable by removing their root cause - poor eating habits!

How to Increase Your Fiber Intake:

A diet based on a variety of fresh, unprocessed foods and an abundance of organic fruits and vegetables should easily provide about 40 grams of fiber a day. This is the recommended amount for adult men and women. According to the American Cancer Society, Americans only consume about 11 grams daily (on average). This is about one-fourth of what is recommended!

Fiber helps to keep your digestive system running smoothly, which in turn helps to increase energy and mental clarity, and can reduce the risk of certain types of cancer. If your diet is lacking in fiber, try these simple steps:

• Eat more fruits, especially berries - toss onto cereal, into yogurt, and keep a piece of fruit with you for an easy, healthful snack.

• Increase vegetable consumption, especially beans -

replace meat dishes with beans (or go half and half), make bean soups and chili, and have beans as a side dish with meals.

• Eat more whole grains. Ready-made cereals can be good fiber sources (look for 4 or 5 grams of bran per one-ounce serving), and try wild and brown rice instead of the traditional white varieties.

• Incorporate freshly ground flax seeds into your diet. Add a tablespoon or two on top of cooked cereal, rice, or yogurt. Put a couple of tablespoons into a fruit smoothie.

How to Increase Your Omega-3 Fatty Acid Intake:

• Increase your intake of fresh fish high in Omega-3. These include salmon (but not canned), tuna steak (not canned), trout, cod and other cold water fish.

• Incorporate freshly ground flax seeds into your diet. Add a tablespoon or two on top of cooked cereal, rice, soup, eggs or yogurt. Put a couple of tablespoons into a fruit smoothie.

• Of the nuts, walnuts contain the most Omega-3 fats. consume a handful of raw (not roasted) for breakfast or a snack.

• Whole grains such as wheat, oats, and barley contain small amounts of Omega-3 fatty acids but only from freshly ground grains consumed the same day it is ground. After that it quickly begins to go rancid. Flax seeds contain the highest level of Omega-3 fats in grains. To obtain the benefits of these essential fatty acids, it is best to purchase the seeds and grind small amounts every day as you need them. After the protective shell of the seed is broken, heat, light and oxygen begin to oxidize the sensitive fats.

When adding ground flax to foods it is best to add it at the table rather than at the stove as the high heat will break down the fats. It is also OK to add ground flax to the batter or dough for baked goods - breads, muffins, pancakes, waffles. etc. (The heat is not as high as on the stove top.) It is best if they are consumed that day.

How to Increase Your Mineral Intake:

• Increase your intake of fresh natural unprocessed foods: fruits, vegetables, grains (including flax), etc.

• Supplement coral calcium or other mineral supplement providing all the minerals in the body not just the top 5 or 10. There are almost 80 minerals in the body and we need all of them. We get them by eating the foods grown in the soil (dust of the earth)!

Q: Why do we need to eat organic?

A: I choose organic foods because they are the closest we have available to the way God intended those foods to be. Therefore, they are better for us. In the United States we have organic certifiers like the California Certified Organic Farmers, Organic Trade Association, Quality Assurance International and the U.S. Department of Agriculture's National Organic Program; in the United Kingdom, the Soil Association is the leading certifier. These following additional reasons for eating organic are based on international organic standards:

1. It's healthier. Organic food tends to contain higher levels (even double in most cases) of vitamin C, cancer-fighting

antioxidants, and all essential minerals including calcium, magnesium, iron and chromium.

2. Organic foods contain no nasty additives. Organic food doesn't contain food additives that can cause health problems such as heart disease, osteoporosis, migraines and hyperactivity (ADD/ADHD).

3. It avoids pesticides. More than 400 chemical pesticides are routinely used in conventional farming and residues are often present in non-organic food.

4. No genetic modification. Under organic standards, genetically modified (GM) crops and ingredients are not allowed.

How do you know if your food is genetically modified? Over 70% of processed foods in the United States contain genetically modified ingredients. The products are not labeled as such, but there are ways to find out if your food has been genetically modified. If your package does not say "NON-GMO" it most likely is Genetically Modified. Sad, but true!

5. There is not a reliance on drugs. Organic farming standards prohibit the routine use of antibiotics and growth hormones in farm animals.

6. Organic produce is a better cancer fighter. A University of California, study of organically grown corn, strawberries, and marion berries found that they contained higher levels of natural cancer-fighting compounds than conventionally grown samples. Pesticides and herbicides used on conventional produce appear to impede the production of phenolics, which defend plants from insects and people from disease.

> *Did you know that researchers estimate that to obtain the level of nutrients provided in a serving of spinach in the 1940's, today we would have to consume **50 times more** because of mineral depletion of the soil!*

Q: Is it safe to eat fish because of the mercury and contamination problem?

A: People often ask me about the safety of eating fish more than once a month - as I recommend it at least once per week. Below is a summary of the findings of the Food and Drug Administration (FDA) and the Environmental Protection Agency (EPA), as listed in an April, 2001 report issued by the Environmental Working Group (EWG) and the U.S. Public Interest Research Group (USPIRG):

My comments are in *(italics)*.

FISH LOWEST IN MERCURY CONTAMINATION
Safest options!

Trout (farmed)

Catfish (farmed) - *(unclean by Levitical law)*

Fish Sticks *(This is questionable in my opinion as this option most likely contains trans fatty acids due to partially hydrogenated or hydrogenated vegetable oil ingredients.)*

Flounder (summer)

Salmon (wild Pacific)

Croaker

Haddock

MODERATE RISK OF CONTAMINATION

Canned tuna

Mahi mahi

Blue mussel *(unclean according to Levitical law)*

Eastern oyster *(unclean according to Levitical law)*

Cod

Pollock

Great Lakes salmon *(Great Lakes fish should be avoided all together because of the high level of industry near the waters)*

Gulf Coast blue crab *(unclean by Levitical law)*

Channel catfish (wild) *(unclean by Levitical law)*

Lake whitefish

HIGHEST RISK OF CONTAMINATION

Avoid or only eat occasionally
(Larger fish tend to be at higher risk)

Shark *(unclean according to Levitical law)*

Swordfish *(unclean according to Levitical law)*

King mackerel

Tilefish

Tuna steaks

Sea bass

Gulf Coast oysters *(unclean by Levitical law)*

Marlin

Halibut

Pike

Walleye

White croaker

Large mouth bass

Obviously, there are many types of fish not men-tioned in the above list. AND.. we often do not know where the fish comes from when we purchase it. Fish from the Gulf and the Great Lakes seem to be the most highly contaminated so should be avoided. Unclean fish and seafood, especially bottom feeders such as shrimp, crap, scallops, crayfish, etc. should be avoided because they were not even created to be food, but were created by God to CLEAN the waters from pollutants!!!! It's no surprise that they would have high levels of mercury and other toxins! It just means they are doing their job!

Q: How does one change from the way one has been eating for years... or their whole life even, to "God's way?" It sounds like a lot of work.

A: First, pray for revelation. Ask the Holy Spirit to show you the importance of treating your body like a temple of the Living God. Ask God is there are any foods He wants you to give up and start there. Fasting is an excellent way to break any food strongholds in your life. God will surely bless you if your heart is right and you are TRYING! Just listen and obey!

Here are a few suggestions. Switch from:

Margarine to **butter or olive oil**

French fries to **baked or roasted potatoes**

Fast food to **home-cooked meals**

Pasta or white rice to **brown or wild rice**

Ready-to-eat breakfast cereals to **whole grain cereals or raw nuts**

Chips and snack food to **raw nuts, home-made granola or raw fruits or vegetables**

Candy to **fruit**

Pop to **water or tea**

White bread to **whole grain bread**

Processed bread to **home-made bread**

Red meat (in excess) to **fish and chicken**

Meat (in excess) to **beans and lentils**

Conventional meat to **free-range grass-fed meat**

Frying to **roasting, broiling, steaming or grilling**

Processed dairy products to **organic fresh natural dairy products, preferably raw,** (unpasteurized and not homogenized)

Conventional eggs to free-range, organic eggs

Fried and scrambled eggs to **poached, soft boiled or hard boiled**

SIMPLE TIPS FOR EATING OUT

We seem to be surrounded by coffee shops, fast food restaurants, convenient stores. All kinds of places to buy food, yet when you go inside there is scarcely a healthy meal to be found. Trying to eat healthy while maintaining a busy a schedule can be a challenging aspects of keeping a nutritious diet.

The first step in choosing a healthy meal is being able to distinguish between real food (made by God) and a concoction of artificial ingredients that would never exist in nature (made by man... also known as fake food). Hints:

1. Real food rarely comes in a box, bag or can so beware of these items when you're shopping for groceries.

2. Real food does not have a long list of "ingredients" - it may have a label to identify it such as "russet" potatoes or "granny smith" apples.

3. If you cannot pronounce the items listed in the ingredient list this is another clue to skip it.

4. Real food usually has a very short shelf life... compared to 2 or even 5 years! The exception to this is dried peas, beans and lentils. Note on the package that no other ingredients are listed.

It's lunch time, and you're narrowed down your "healthiest" choices to a salad, a tuna sandwich or an energy bar...think of the following recommendations:

Choose the Salad, but Don't Forget Protein:

A salad is generally a healthy choice for lunch, especially if you load it up with organic greens, fresh vegetables and beans or nuts. However, remember that your hunger won't be satisfied for long if you don't add protein such as chicken, eggs, nuts, or beans.

If you're making your salad on-the-go, be careful with the commercial salad dressings on most salad bars. They are typically full of trans fat (partially hydrogenated oils), sugar and other scary ingredients. Don't ruin a healthy salad with processed dressing. Choose olive oil, lemon juice or vinegar instead.

Beware of the Bread:

No matter what the meal, you're better off without the bread if it's made from white flour (devoid of most the nutrients we need to properly process the carbohydrates that remain), highly processed and contains who knows what else. Watch out for "hidden" bread in breading, toppings, stuffing, soups and croutons.

Pass on the Fries, White Bread and Pasta:

Most restaurants serve the main dish along with a potato, pasta or other starch, but that doesn't mean you have to accept it. Ask them to substitute vegetables instead, and you'll be doing your health and blood sugar a big favor. Most restaurants are happy to make the substitution.

Skip the Sauce:

Most sauces contain added sugars and other chemicals. This includes ketchup, mayonnaise, barbecue sauce, sandwich spreads, fast food sauces, glazes and other condiments like sweet pickles. You're better off ordering your food served plain, and then adding some healthy flavor like lemon, lime, vinegar, garlic or herbs.

Choose the Least Offensive Cooking Method:

Rule out the items "fried," "crispy," and "charbroiled." All of these words mean that the food will be cooked in a way resulting in many lost nutrients. There is also the issue of trans fatty acids and acrylamide, potentially cancer-causing chemicals, that are found in a wide range of fried foods.

Look for steamed, poached, slow-cooked or other light cooking methods. Try to consume at least one-third of your food raw, as this is the form that will give you the maximum amount of nutrients.

Drink Water:

Don't ruin your attempts for a healthy meal with a soda, diet soda or other sugar-filled beverage along with your meal. Drinking pure water or green tea with your meal, as opposed to soda, fruit juice or coffee, is an easy way to stay hydrated and healthy.

FOODS THAT...

Nourish:

Fruits, fresh if possible

Vegetables, fresh if possible

Whole grains

Beans, lentils, etc.

Raw dairy products

Organic meats, poultry and fish

Nuts

Water

Deplete:

Sugar, sweets, many desserts

Pop or soda

Most "fast food"

Fried foods

Trans fatty acids (found in hydrogenated oils and fried foods)

Fake foods like margarine and canola oil

Coffee, black tea

Refined foods

Chips

Instant breakfast cereals

Alcohol

Artificial colors

Artificial flavors

MSG, and other preservatives and additives

THINGS THAT...

Nourish:

Prayer

Worship

Study of God's Word

Family time

Playing with children

Working the land

Fruitful hobbies, i.e. gardening, horseback riding, painting,

Going for nature walks or bike rides-enjoying all God has created

Jesus

Deplete:

Television (most secular)

Many movies

Drunkenness

Carousing (bars, parties, etc.)

Foul language

Arguing

Yelling

Unforgiveness

Immorality

Pornography

Course joking

Making fun of people

Gossip

Gluttony

Workaholic attitude

Envy

Pharmaceuticals and other drugs

Smoking

Sin

Rebellion

Satan

QUALITY WHOLE FOODS...
FOR LIFE

The closer the food is to the natural state in which God made it, or the closer to its raw, unrefined form, the higher its nutritional quality. In this condition, all the enzymes are found intact. The amino acids are in their finest form. The minerals, vitamins, trace elements, carbohydrates, essential fatty acids, enzymes, phytochemicals, antioxidants and total "life force" are present. The life force, in turn, is capable of repro-ducing healthy tissue. The body is constantly in a state of healing and repair and needs these superior quality raw materials to form superior quality tissues and cells in our body.

The quality of a nutritional program is also improved by omitting toxic substances such as tobacco, table salt (sodium chloride), hydrogenated vegetable oils, sugar, corn syrup, other processed sweeteners as well as aspartame, saccharin and other artificial sweeteners, dyes and coloring, preserva-tive, and all other chemicals from your diet.

The goal is to introduce foods of higher quality in place of lower quality ones. Replace pork and beef with organic poultry and wild-caught fish. Replace processed cheese with natural, organic raw milk cheese. Then eliminate processed snack foods with raw unsalted nuts and seeds or dried an fresh fruit.

The key is to NOT be overwhelmed at how bad you think your diet is, but to **commit to starting an improvement plan.** Then, start with one thing...just one thing! For example, to eliminate all hydrogenated vegetable oils (trans fats) from your diet or to stop using the microwave (better yet throw it out). Focus on that for a time, then add a few thing like eliminating all artificial and processed sweeteners, replacing them with stevia, honey, maple syrup or agave nectar. Then focus on eliminating all artificial colors and flavors and other additives, replacing those foods with whole, fresh foods.

Food choices are always in front of you. Keep in mind, one choice will lead to discomfort and disease and the other leads to restoration, health and enjoyable life. It is never too late to improve your health.

Many people cringe at the idea of eating unfamiliar vegetables, such as arugula, mustard greens, turnips, etc. This is often a result of never having eaten these foods prepared in an appetizing and satisfying way. There are many foods I thought I didn't like until I prepared them in a way that was pleasing to my taste buds. This is why I have included many delicious recipes for you to try. If they are not to your taste - adjust them until you find a way that you like them! I believe cooking is meant to be creative. Have fun!

Our physiological makeup (how our body is made and how it works, how we process food, etc) is essentially the same as our forefathers. So if we have the same body types and we process our food the same way as our great grandparents and great-great grandparents, how can we expect the same healthy outcome from eating a diet very different from what they ate? Our ancestors never had access to and never ate the processed, irradiated, genetically engineered, refined and synthetic (man-made) and "fake" "foods" eaten today.

Consider what would happen if you substitute soda pop or Kool-Aid in your washing machine instead of water. How much longer would it work?

What happens if you feed french fries to a horse, Krispy Kreme to a cow, assorted chemicals to a human? What happens when we substitute synthetic 'FAKE" products for the many different nutrients that our cells and internal organs simply need to function well?

The very sad consequences of the latest generations' food choices is becoming more apparent every day as we are now seeing chronic diseases become epidemic in our society. Health problems largely unheard of 100 years ago are reaching epidemic levels: ADD/ADHD, autism, Alzheimer's, Irritable Bowel, Chronic Fatigue, and on and on. All of these can be associated to diet - omega-3 fatty acids deficiency, lack of fiber, minerals and an abundance of man-made CHEMICALS that do not belong in the body.

The United States has the worst health status (life expectancy, morbidity, obesity and infant mortality) of any of the industrialized nations, yet we spend the most money on "healthcare" and take the most pharmaceuticals. Americans are getting sicker and sicker while taking more and more drugs!

It's NOT too expensive to eat healthy!

Consider this: A trip to a large fast food chain restaurant costs over $17.00 for four sandwiches and four "regular fries." For $17.00 after removing all the packaging you get 2.80 pounds, net weight, of "food." This is over $6.00 per pound, which is triple the average price of organic foods in a typical health food store. For some reason most people are under the false impression that fast food is cheap, and organic food is expensive!

Here are a few tips to reduce the cost of your healthy shopping:

1. Organic produce and food items are usually less expensive in local co-ops or a health food store like Mother's, Wild Oats or Whole Foods Markets, compared to regular grocery stores that only have a small natural foods section of the store. Also, you will find that the produce in the health food store is much fresher and usually of better quality.

2. Shopping through a group co-op will allow you to buy organic foods at wholesale prices. For more information on co-ops, see pages 49 and 59.

Forget what you ate until today. What you eat FROM NOW ON is vitally important to your continued well-being.

Only a few generations ago, our ancestors were very fit and healthy compared with today. The majority lived good, active, healthy lives and ultimately died peacefully in their sleep. Today that is a rarity. Whereas chronic disease, chronic pain, and prolonged end-of-life care were rare for our ancestors, it is becoming much more the expected outcome for us. What is the single difference between these two centuries? The overwhelmingly different factor in our lives is the refined, processed, chemical products and man-made foods that we eat, that our ancestors simply did not eat.

Vegetables: Maximize Whole Vegetables
Vegetables are best organic and either raw or minimally cooked. The more vegetables you eat, the have less room

you will have for junk.

If you can't find much fresh organic food in your area, try looking into a local co-op or Community Supported Agriculture. This is a fast growing movement of small local farms throughout the United States that sell fresh seasonal food, usually organic, by subscription. You either pick it up at the farm or at an intermediate location, or they deliver to you. *See www.csacenter.org or www.diamondorganics.com/*

Organic food right from the field is FAR superior in taste and nutritional value compared to produce that has been sitting around for weeks or worse, that came off an assembly line overlooking the industrial landscape surrounding the New Jersey turnpike. Freshness and taste and the deepest satisfaction of your body's basic metabolic needs.

Try to get as many different colors into your meals as possible! Make salads containing dark green spinach, red, orange and yellow bell pepper, red and yellow tomatoes, green snap peas, red dried cranberries, green cucumber, red cabbage, orange carrots, green serrano and jalapeno peppers, green broccoli, green asparagus, etc.

Green vegetables are such a staple of a healthy diet that they should be eaten EVERY DAY. However, wonderful as green vegetables are, they do not provide the full spectrum of nutrients. Remember also the orange vegetables, such as carrots, sweet potato, squash, pumpkin and orange bell pepper, which provide the very important flavonoids. Red vegetables, such as tomatoes, are also important for lycopene.

Our bodies depend upon a rich variety of healthy foods. Such nutrients are not available in processed and junk food.

Vegetables are one of the most underrated components of a healthy diet. Not only do these supply incredible amounts of nutrients and fiber, they are rich with water and can help with hydration and contain various chemicals that have been shown to fight cancer and other illnesses.

- Arugula
- Asparagus
- Bamboo shoots
- Bean sprouts
- Beet greens
- Bell peppers
- Broccoli
- Brussels sprouts
- Cabbage
- Carrots
- Cauliflower
- Celery
- Chicory
- Chives
- Collard greens
- Cowpeas
- Cucumber
- Dandelion greens
- Eggplant
- Fennel
- Garlic
- Ginger root
- Gourd
- Green beans
- Kale
- Lettuce (the darker in color, the better)
- Mushrooms
- Mustard greens
- Onions
- Parsley
- Peppers - all! jalapeno, serrano, habanero, etc.
- Radishes
- Radicchio
- Scallop squash

- Snap beans
- Snow peas
- Spinach
- Spaghetti squash (great to use instead of pasta)
- Summer squash
- Zucchini
- Tomatoes
- Turnip greens
- Watercress

While this is by no means an all-inclusive list. In general, simply focus on buying, preparing and eating whole, unprocessed foods as much as possible.

Fruits: Eat Them Whole and Natural

Fruits are excellent and nutrient-packed as well. Fruits should also be eaten in their whole, natural state as much as possible, and avoided in any concentrated form. Fruit juice, jams, jellies, and other fruit-based processed foods are so concentrated with sugar that they produce high insulin responses. Insulin rushes are the very most important thing you need to avoid in order to maintain good health and appropriate weight.

Have a rainbow of whole fruits for the same reason as having a rainbow of vegetables. You need the nutrients that are represented in the various colors.

Carbohydrates

Carbohydrates (grains, fruit, vegetables, etc.) are not the evil they have been made out to be. healthy carbs contain less simple sugars and higher complex giving them a lower glycemic index rating:

Healthy (low glycemic index) carbohydrates:

- Applesauce (natural, no sugar added)
- Apples
- Artichokes
- Avocados - also rich in healthy fats
- Potato (red is better than white)
- Bananas (not over-ripe)
- Barley
- Beets
- Black beans - also excellent for protein and fiber
- Blackberries
- Blueberries (very high in antioxidants)
- Brown rice, but wild rice is best!
- Buckwheat
- Carrots
- Cherries
- Chickpeas - also excellent for protein and fiber
- Corn
- Green beans
- Grapefruit
- Grapes
- Green peas
- Groats
- Kidney beans
- Kiwi
- Leeks
- Lemons
- Lentils - one of nature's "perfect" foods
- Lima beans
- Limes
- Mangos
- Navy beans
- Oats - steel-cut or whole is best
- Okra
- Oranges

- Parsnip
- Peaches
- Pears
- Pinto beans - avoid high-sodium canned,
- Plain whole yogurt - excellent source of protein, carbohydrates, and healthy fats.
- Plums
- Pumpkin - also contains healthy fat
- Quinoa
- Raspberries
- Rye
- Squash
- Strawberries
- Sweet potato
- Tangerines
- Turnips
- Wheat

Protein: Meats, Dairy, Eggs, Nuts, Legumes, Seeds

If you are a meat eater, then consume high quality meat. Your best choices are organic, free-range meats. The more people ask for these in supermarkets, the more supermarkets will begin to carry them. Buffalo and venison are very nutritious. Roasting and grilling is better than frying.

Healthy Sources of Proteins

Protein foods are the main source of amino acids in the diet. Examples include:
- All "clean" fish (cold water fish is preferred as they contain higher levels of healthy fats)
- Buffalo
- Chicken
- Cottage cheese

- Eggs
- Lamb (leaner cuts or in moderation)
- Lean beef
- Turkey
- Venison

Always buy organic, wild, or free range if possible!

Eggs and organic and raw cheese and milk will be beneficial to some and allergenic to others. It is best to pay attention to your body and watch for symptoms after eating dairy and eggs. (The most highly allergenic foods are dairy, wheat, eggs, soy, citrus, peanuts and corn. That doesn't mean that you should avoid all of them, but these 7 foods are less digestible than others, so watch for feelings of fatigue or discomfort after eating them, even 12-24 hours later.)

Snack on nuts and seeds. Walnuts, pecans, almonds, hazelnuts, cashews, pumpkin seeds, sunflower seeds, as well as butters made from seeds and nuts are very highly nutritious and should be eaten frequently, unless one is allergic. Walnuts, high in omega-3 fatty acids, are a very important brain food for everyone, especially children. Other foods high in omega-3 fatty acids are flaxseed, grass-fed beef and salmon.

Healthy Fats

Fats are a very important part of the diet needed for many things in the body including production of hormones and many other chemicals and all of our cells, especially in the brain. Healthy fats include:
- Almonds and natural almond butter
- Butter
- Cheese (Natural! not the processed fake stuff)
- Macadamia nuts
- Olive oil
- Peanuts and all natural peanut butter
- Pecans
- Pistachio nuts

- Pumpkin and squash seeds
- Safflower kernels
- Sunflower butter
- Sunflower seed
- Walnuts

This is not a temporary fix... it's a way of life!

The only kind of diet that will do you any good is one that you can be comfortable with long-term. Don't count calories, carbs.. You could drive yourself up a wall trying to figure out how many this or that you are eating or should eat.

The goal is to have such a well balanced and therefore satisfying diet, that there is nothing wanting and thus no need to cheat. The higher the quality of food we eat, the quicker we recover from disease, provided we are able to digest and assimilate properly.

We Reap What We Sow!!

What happens when a person improves the quality of food consumed? Remarkable things begin to happen to the body as well as the mind. The body is designed to heal itself... when we provide it with the nutrients for it to do what it was designed to do... it does it!!

When the quality of the food coming into the body is of higher quality than the tissues which the body is made of, the body begins to discard the lower grade materials and tissues to make room for the superior materials which it uses to make new and healthier tissue.

This is how God created us! The body is very selective and always tries to produce health and always will, unless our interference is too great. Only then do we fail to recover and degenerate further into disease. The self-curing nature of many conditions such as colds, fevers, cuts, swellings, injuries, etc., furnishes endless examples of how the body tends towards health--always--unless we do something to stop the process.

To a lesser extent, the same process occurs when we abandon lower quality foods and replace them with better foods. When some people stop eating "junk" and begin to eat real food, the body may go through some unpleasant "detox" activities as the body is getting rid of toxins which have been stored or a long time:

Headaches and intestinal gas may occur at the beginning; fever and/or colds; the skin may break out; bowel sluggishness, occasional diarrhea, feelings of fatigue and weakness, disinclination to exercise, nervousness, irritability, negativity or mental depression, frequent urination, etc.

This is just the body's way of housecleaning - and it is temporary. My only suggestion is to make sure you are drinking enough water to flush out the toxins.

Those who have abused their bodies less will likely have reactions from almost none or very mild. Those who have lived very toxic lives may experience more severe symptoms if their liver, kidneys, or other important eliminating organs have been damaged. When they have been restored to the point of fair working order, they will no longer produce symptoms.

The great majority of people find their reactions tolerable and are encouraged to bear with them because of the many improvements which have already occurred and are becoming more evident with each day.

Be happy you are getting rid of what does not belong in the body and what has been hampering you from reaching optimal health. The mysteries of the body, the operations of nature, the vital forces working in nature are far beyond what our minds are prepared to understand at present. Every great physician or scientist has marvelled in awe and humility at the wonders of the human body. Yes, we are "*fearfully and wonderfully made!*" Psalms 139.

COOKING WHOLE FOOD FROM SCRATCH...
<u>NOT</u> that Difficult!

Whole fresh foods should be the basis of what we all eat. Whole foods, whether meat, vegetable or fruit, do two things: they provide all the nutrients that nature put into the food--not just as a sum of nutrients, but even more, as a synergy of nutrients that work together because they naturally interact within the living plant or animal. When we eat these foods, which have been connected with our whole existence as a species, the total health benefit to us is much greater than the sum of the parts. The second practical advantage of eating whole fresh foods is that they substitute, by their sheer bulk, the chemicals and denatured food derivatives that we might otherwise eat.

But what do you do if you work non-stop and when you get home there is no time or energy to do anything but further destroy half-synthetic processed food in the microwave? Here are several ideas you can use to streamline your efforts and maximize the productivity of your kitchen.

Remember, when shopping at the market, stay around the periphery where the whole foods are located. This will save time (from going up and down the interior aisles where the processed foods are) and also reduce temptation from taking those things home.

In the kitchen cook enough so that there are leftovers. Leftovers can be frozen, eaten the next evening or taken to work for lunch. Cooking several large meals (a pan of vegetable lasagna and chicken parmesan with wild rice, a large kettle of soup, etc.) on the weekend can give you enough meals for most of the following week so all you have to do is reheat the leftovers.

I do not recommend reheating with a microwave which destroys nutrients and actually creates carcinogens (cancer causing agents). Microwave radiation also leaks throughout the whole kitchen from most microwave ovens, which creates an unhealthy atmosphere for adults, children and pets. To reheat, use a toaster oven, regular oven or stovetop. Heating leftovers for two or three people in a toaster oven or stovetop does not take much longer than a microwave, while preserving it's nutrients.

Invest in a good-sized thermos (glass or stainless steel, **not** aluminum) for each family member. While eating breakfast, heat up leftovers and spoon it into each thermos. In each lunchbox, add a fork and small containers of nuts or some fresh fruit or vegetables.

Nutritious, well balanced and appetizing lunches can quickly and easily be made for every family member.

Cooking big/freezing small is also a great way for a single person to enjoy healthy home-cooked meals.

Involve the Whole Family:

Children of various ages can be recruited to help. Toddlers can peel carrots, while older children can wash and chop foods. Working together in the kitchen teaches unity, cooperation and passes the tradition to the next generation so that cooking does not become just another lost art.

TIPS ON RESOURCES
"Where do I get that?"

A commonly asked question I get when I am teaching about natural foods or recipes and ingredients is "**Where do I get that?**"

Depending on where you live, finding natural food items can be more or less difficult.. When I lived in southern California, it was very easy with health food stores in abundance offering beautiful fresh organic produce and even raw milk. When I moved to northern Minnesota. I had a very difficult time finding the foods I wanted. So here are some suggestions:

Health food stores or the health food section of your regular grocery stores will carry many of the items you are looking for. This ia a great way to try out something new. Ask them to carry items if they don't. The down side of this is you will probably pay a premium price.

Buy direct in bulk (and pay wholesale prices). For example, I buy my wild rice direct in 5, 10 or 25 lb quantities. Find a brand or supplier you like and call them direct to see if they will sell to you in bulk, where you will get a much better price.

Co-ops: In a small town you may need to ask around to find out if there is already one started. If there is not, you can easily start one yourself with a small group of people. Go to **http://www.unitedbuyingclubs.com/** and get all the details you need to get started. With a co-op individuals order items in bulk together, usually monthly. The cost is much less than shopping in a health food store. The variety and selection of foods is much greater as well.

Buy local: Look for signs or flyers hanging in the health food stores for farm-fresh eggs, organic beef, etc. or ask the manager, or even better, **grow your own!!**

HEALTHY ALTERNATIVES...

For homogenized, pasteurized milk:
Raw milk - straight from the dairy!
Almond milk (*recipe on page 189*)

For white sugar:
Honey
Maple syrup (Real, of course)
Stevia (Natural, no calories, no effect on blood sugar)
Apple sauce or fruit juice
Agave nectar (Natural high fructose fruit juice, lower effect on blood sugar)

For pasta:
Wild Rice
Barley - cook it like rice
Spaghetti squash
Cabbage leaves (for manicotti or lasagna)

For boxed or instant breakfast cereal:
Oats or steel-cut oats - This can even be made in the crock pot on low setting during the night while you sleep! Throw in some raisins, chopped or dried apple, cinnamon and maple syrup! Yum!

Cream of wheat cereal - made by grinding your wheat berries (can even be done in a coffee bean grinder), adding water or milk, a pinch of sea salt and cooking on the stove top for a few minutes. Top with some fresh organic butter and you'll never go back to the processed boxed stuff!

Raw almonds - about 1/2 cup + 2-3 tablespoons of dried cranberries or other dried fruit.
Smoothies *(recipes starting on page 86)*
Ezekiel bread *(recipe on page 160)* **with a soft boiled egg or natural cheese** (even melted!)
Hard boiled eggs (can be made days in advance)

These balanced foods do not spike your insulin levels, unlike so many other dishes that we unfortunately have become accustomed to thinking of as breakfast foods.

For salt: Season foods with:

Lemon or lime juice
Apple cider or balsamic vinegar
Bragg's Liquid Amino's
Garlic, cayenne pepper, other herbs
Sea salt

We Are Made of The Dust *(Minerals)* of the Earth! Genesis 2:9

Sea salt is natural (made from sea water) and contains **many** minerals found in the body and is actually good for you compared to highly processed sodium chloride (commonly known as table salt).

Natural sea salt is a source of 21 essential and 30 trace minerals that are **essential** to our health (and naturally present in the body). Refined table salt contains **less than 0.5%** other minerals.

Using table salt (containing only the one mineral, sodium) actually creates a need for MORE of the other minerals because the minerals all need to be in balance with each other.

For pop:
Water
Lemon water
Lemonaid made with stevia *(recipe on page 189)*
Herbal tea (hot or cold)

For ice cream:
Make your own from real raw milk and honey!

Plain non-fat organic YOGURT topped with fresh fruit such as blueberries, strawberries, sliced nectarines. etc. Sprinkle on some freshly ground flax seed and a light drizzle of honey or maple syrup and you are set for a feast.

Smoothies (Fruity, cool, creamy, and nutritionally balanced! So many varieties to choose from. *(Recipes starting on page 86.)*

For processed snack crackers:
It's hard to find healthy crackers that contain all whole grains and NO hydrogenated oils.
Flax crackers - *recipes on pages 167-169.*
Celery - fill with peanut butter, almond
  butter or cream cheese
Tortillas - spread with toppings, warm in
  oven and cut into 4 or 6 pieces.

For Tums® and antacids:
Celery is excellent for heartburn and indigestion relief! Raw celery has an alkaline pH that instantly seems to neutralize and calm down an upset stomach and acidity of heartburn. It's like a natural antacid.

Eating raw sticks or drinking the juice in combination with other "greens", plus apple, carrot, etc. is a great way to alkalize and cure a lot of other problems besides the heartburn!

Note: Eating 5 stalks of celery every day is also excellent for high blood pressure! Celery is rich in minerals our body and heart needs to function at it's best!

For snacks, lunches and travel:

Many snack foods are highly processed, which are lacking in nutrients, fiber and food value. Many of these suggestions can be taken to work for lunch or served to kids any time!

Fresh Fruit
Apples
Pears
Peaches and nectarines
Kiwi - no need to peel them, just slice up like a tomato
Oranges
Mango
Grapes

Got leftovers? **Make an Easy Fruit Salad**
In a large bowl place 1 cup plain non-fat) yogurt. Add 1 or 2 teaspoons stevia and 1 tablespoon lemon juice or vanilla. Add chopped fruit (about 3 cups) and about 1/4 coconut if desired. Toss together and serve chilled.

Dried fruit
Raisins, apples, mango, papaya, etc. make a good snack, but avoid those with sulfites and added sugar.

If you have glucose concerns it is best to not eat dried fruit alone due to it's high glycemic index rating. Combine with protein such as nuts, jerky or cheese.

Raw Nuts - Especially almonds, but all are good when raw and in their natural state.

Fruit/Nut Combo
Combine raw almonds (or other raw nuts) and dried fruit (such as cranberries or cherries) in a plastic baggie for travel.

Trail Mix
Recipe on page 188.

Granola
Healthy natural unsweetened granola can be purchased at health food stores or you can make your own. *Recipe on page 170.*

Jerky
An excellent low fat source of natural protein. Make your own in a dehydrator, low heat oven or smoker, or look for brands containing no preservatives (nitrates, etc.).

Chopped vegetables
Carrot sticks
Jicama
Cucumber slices
Broccoli
Cauliflower
Tomato
Asparagus spears
Cut vegetables into pieces and store in plastic baggie for travel.

Spicy Black Bean Dip
Recipe on page 187.

Lentil Pate
Recipe on page 188.

Cucumber Sandwiches
Place a piece of natural cheese between two
cucumber slices

Celery sticks & nut butter - fill sticks with
freshly ground nut butter (no sugar added) and
freshly ground flax seed
*For travel, you can mix your nut butter and flax
seeds and store in a container and dip your celery
sticks into the mixture!*

Celery sticks & Cheese - fill sticks with cream
cheese or other soft cheese - stir in dried onion,
chopped sun dried tomato, other spices and ground
flax for variety.

To eating at work or while traveling:

Leftovers or soup in a thermos

Salads in a container with a lid

Nuts and dried fruit

**Many fruits do not require refrigeration and can
easily be taken with you.**

This is by no means a complete recipe book. I simply have so many people asking for recipes that I have finally compiled some of my more commonly used "recipes." Keep in mind that when cooking, I hardly ever "follow" recipes, so many of these are largely "approximations" of what I use. I taste and adjust. I look at a few recipes for something and then create what I want... so here are some of my "creations."

*Cooking is about **creating** healthy, good tasting meals out of what is fresh and available to you. So be creative! Don't be afraid! It's fun! It's like painting a picture - combining different flavors AND colors! Cooking is indeed an art!*

Experiment! Substitute! I believe that that the more free you are (with some limits, of course) when cooking, the more enjoyable it is for you AND your hungry table mates.

*Finally, when you are cooking for friends, families, loved ones, etc., **don't forget** the ingredient left out of processed, frozen, packaged, instant, fast food and microwave meals... LOVE!!*

Enjoy! Dr. Beth

What's Cooking... in Beth's Kitchen?

You'll find lots of
Garlic, Spinach,
Wild Rice, Salmon,
Lentils and Beans, Beans,
and more Beans,
Cayenne Pepper, Flax,
Pumpkin, Lemon, Cheese,
Eggs, Ezekiel Bread...
and last but not least, Chocolate!

RECIPE INDEX

BREAKFAST 72

Asparagus Frittata
Zucchini Frittata
Breakfast Veggie Quiche
Carrot Souffle'
Spinach & Mushroom Quiche
Spinach & Mushroom Quiche-2
Poached Huevos Rancheros
Eggs Benedict Florentine
Quiche in Bell Pepper
Breakfast Cookies
Oatmeal Pancakes
Cranberry Pancakes
Beth's Anti-Cholesterol Muffins
Zucchini Oatmeal Muffins
Pumpkin Bread
5-Grain Breakfast
Old Fashioned Portage
Cinnamon Scones

SMOOTHIES 88

Berry Berry Smoothie
Orange Dream Smoothie
Green Detox Smoothie
Apricot Smoothie
Strawberry Banana Smoothie
Mango, Yogurt & Lime
Cantaloupe Smoothie

SALADS 91

Orange-Jicama Salad
Gini's Fruit Salad
Dr. Beth's Fruit Salad
Broccoli Salad

Garlic Coleslaw
Michael's Favorite Coleslaw
Grilled Romaine
Barley Vegetable Salad
Wheat Berry Salad
Roasted Beet & Arugula Salad
Orange Wild Rice Salad
Blood Oranges w/ Green Onion
Mustard Chicken & Arugula
    Salad
Red Cabbage and Apple Salad
Asparagus Avocado Salad
Avocado Salad
Salmon Caesar Salad
Broccoli Salad w/ Oranges
Easy Spinach Mushroom Salad
Spinach Orange Salad
Red Potato Salad

SALAD DRESSINGS 105

Quick and Easy Dressing
Caesar
Buttermilk Dressing
Raspberry-Orange Vinaigrette
Mayonnaise

SPINACH, BEETS, ETC 107

Sauteéd Spinach
Creamed Spinach
Spinach Wild Rice Casserole
Spinach Pie
Indian Creamed Curried Spinach
    with Sag Paneer
Pasta with Spinach Pesto

Swiss Chard
Orange-Roasted Beets &
    Greens

SOUP   116

Sweet Potato Chowder
Old Fashioned Potato Soup
Butternut Wild Rice Soup
Red Lentil and Squash Soup
Cajun Black Bean Soup
Smoked Salmon w/ White Bean
Lentil Soup
Spicy Bean Soup
"Creamy" Carrot Bisque
Spinach Soup
Spinach Supreme Soup
Lemon Chicken Noodle Soup
Orzo, Lentil and Flax Soup
Hearty Bean and Vegetable
    Stew
Thai Tomato Soup
Vegetarian Green Chile
Chickpea and Spinach Soup
with Almonds and Garlic
Texas Red Chili

SIDE DISHES   133

Barbecue Pinto Beans
Pink Lentil Curry
Rosemary Red Potatoes
Parmesan Red Potatoes
Dill Fingerling Potatoes
Roasted Sweet Potatoes with
    Cumin and Cilantro
Crockpot Sweet Potatoes
Candied Yams
Corn Bread
Stuffed Green Peppers

Spanish Rice
Green Bean Casserole

WILD RICE DISHES   142

Wild Rice and Mushrooms
Wild Rice Soup
Broccoli Wild Rice
Wild Rice with Peas and Garlic
Wild Rice Pancakes

LUNCH   147

Turkey Wrap
Quesadilla (Grilled or Baked)
Pita, Feta and Riata

MAIN COURSE   149

Roast Beef or Venison
Garlic Steak w/ Asparagus
Beef or Venison Mushroom
    Burgundy
Lemon Chicken
Chicken Parmesan
Hot Wings
Eggplant Parmesan
Vegetable Lasagna
Black Bean & Cheese Enchiladas
Chicken in Mushroom Sauce
Broccoli Chicken
Orange Glazed Turkey Breast w/
    Cinnamon
Yellow Squash w/ Pasta
Jalapeno Macaroni and Cheese
Fettuccine with Red Pepper
    Sauce
Bison Meat Loaf
Bison Meat Balls
Michael's Bison Patty Melt

RECIPE INDEX CONT.

Spicy Shredded Bison or Chicken

SALMON RECIPES   167

Roasted Salmon
Seared Salmon w/ Orange
     Glaze
Dijon Salmon on Wild Rice
Grilled Salmon w/ Vegetables
Easy Grilled Salmon
Poached Salmon
Citrus Salmon
Fusilli w/ Baked Tomatoes and
     Salmon
Salmon-Broccoli Loaf w/ Dill &
     Capers
Salmon Limone
Herbed Poached Salmon
Spicy Salmon and Eggplant
Thai Salmon Parcels

OTHER TYPES OF FISH 177

Orange Teriyaki Tuna
Grilled Seared Tuna with Basil
     Butter
Baked Parmesan Crusted Cod
     with Spinach

EZEKIEL BREAD   180

Almond Ezekiel Bread
Orange-Coconut Ezekiel Bread
Focaccia (Italian-Herb Bread)
Pizza Crust or Bread Sticks
Thin Crust Pizza

FLAX RECIPES   184

Flax Fruit Bars
Flax Almond Cookies
Flax Oatmeal Cookies
Whole Wheat Flax Bread
Banana-Date Flax Seed Bread
Toasted Flax
Apple Flax Pudding
Veggie Flax Seed Crackers
Flax Crackers #1
Flaxseed Crackers #2
Granola

DESSERTS   193

Low Fat Cheese Cake w/
     Raspberry Lemon Topping
Lemon Cheesecake
Rhubarb Cheesecake
Pumpkin Cheesecake
Chocolate Cheesecake
Fruit Tart or Fruit Pizza
Chocolate Silk Pie
Almond Maple Pie Crust
Graham Cracker Crust
Butter Pie Crust
Rhubarb Crumble Pie
Chocolate Chip Zucchini Cake
Meyer Lemon Buttermilk
     Pudding Cake w/ Berries
Low Fat Lemon Bars
Pumpkin-Nut Loaf
Chocolate Chocolate Chip
     Cookies
Chocolate Orange Tart

Apple Oat Bars
Dr. Beth's Carrot Cake
Apricot Pudding Cake
Cinnamon Raisin Rice Pudding
Chocolate Chestnut Mousse
Fruit Dip
Rhubarb Sauce

MISCELLANEOUS   215

Salsa
Spicy Black Bean Dip
Lentil Pate
Hummus
White Cheese Jalapeno Dip
Trail Mix

Granola
Cream Cheese
Yogurt
Whipped Cream

BEVERAGES   220

Hot Harvest Cider
Fresh Lemonade
Almond Milk

A KEY TO HEALTHY COOKING...

Use fresh, natural, high-quality ingredients.

This means using organic whenever possible. Any extra (perceived) cost is well worth it... in taste and in nutritional value.

Remember, with organic foods, in many cases you get (at least) double the quantity of nutrients.

BREAKFAST

I use the "term" breakfast loosely because I make many of these foods for any meal of the day!

Asparagus Frittata

Frittata are the Italian interpretation of French omelets. Serve frittata with fruit for breakfast or with a salad and Ezekiel bread for lunch or dinner.

Ingredients
- 8 oz. pencil thin asparagus, tough stems trimmed
- Olive oil
- 4 shallots, thinly sliced
- 4 large eggs
- 2 large egg whites
- 1 tablespoon snipped chives, optional
- 1/4 teaspoon sea salt and freshly ground black pepper
- 2 tablespoons freshly grated Parmesan cheese

1. Cut asparagus spears into 2 1/2-inch (7.5-cm) lengths. Bring a saucepan of water to a boil and cook the asparagus until just tender, about 2 minutes. Drain and place in a bowl.

2. Preheat the broiler.

3. Oil a 9 or 10-inch nonstick ovenproof skillet and set over medium-low heat. Add shallots and cook, stirring, until they begin to brown, about 2 minutes. Add the shallots to the asparagus.

4. In a mixing bowl, whisk together eggs, egg whites, chives, salt and pepper. Add asparagus/shallot mixture.

5. Oil the skillet generously and return the skillet to the heat. When the pan is hot, pour in the egg mixture and gently shake the pan to evenly distribute the vegetables. Reduce heat to medium-low and cook until the bottom is set, about 5 minutes.

6. Sprinkle the top of the frittata with Parmesan and place under the broiler to finish cooking, about 1-2 minutes.

7. Cut into wedges and serve.

Zucchini Frittata

8 oz. zucchini, chopped
Olive oil
4 shallots, thinly sliced
4 large eggs
2 large egg whites
1-2 cloves chopped garlic
1 teaspoon dried oregano
1/4 teaspoon sea salt and freshly ground black pepper
1/2 cup freshly grated Parmesan cheese

Estimated cooking time: Under 30 minutes
1.   Preheat the broiler.
2.   Oil a 9 or 10-inch nonstick ovenproof skillet and set over medium-low heat. Add shallots and garlic and cook, stirring, until they begin to brown, about 2 minutes. Add zucchini to the shallots and garlic and cook for a few more minutes.
3. In a mixing bowl, whisk together eggs, egg whites, chives, oregano, salt and pepper. Add zucchini/shallot/garlic mixture and about 1/2 of the cheese.
4.   Oil skillet generously and return the skillet to the heat. When the pan is hot, pour in the egg mixture and gently shake the pan to evenly distribute the vegetables. Reduce the heat to medium-low and cook until the bottom is set, about 5 minutes.
5.   Sprinkle the top of the frittata with the remaining cheese and place under the broiler to finish cooking, about 1-2 minute.
6.   Cut into wedges and serve.

Breakfast Veggie Quiche

1 small onion - chopped fine
1 cup sliced mushrooms
1/2 cup finely chopped bell peppers or other veggies.
Saute in olive oil - and set aside to cool a little
2 1/2 cups spinach or grated zucchini)

Mix together:
5 eggs and 2 egg whites
1 box tofu
1/2 cup grated cheese
1/4 cup parmesan cheese
1 tsp sea salt
1 teaspoon Cajun seasoning
Splash of salsa or tabasco (optional)

Pour into square glass baking dish and bake in oven at 375 degrees F for about 45 minutes. Cover for first 30 minutes then remove cover for browning the last 15 minutes. I like to serve with salsa and sour cream, but it's not necessary.

Carrot Souffle'

2 lbs carrots, boiled in water and pureed
2 Tablespoons onion, finely chopped
1/4 cup butter
2 teaspoons lemon juice
1/4 teaspoon stevia or 2 tablespoons honey
1 tablespoon flour
1 teaspoon sea salt
1/2 teaspoon cinnamon
1 cup milk (or 1/2 cup 1/2 and 1/2)
5 eggs

Mix together and bake in greased casserole dish (approx. 7x10 inches) for one hour at 350. Serve with toasted Ezekiel Bread or Banana-Date Flax Seed Bread!

Spinach & Mushroom Quiche

4 eggs
1 1/2 cups cooked rice
3 oz grated cheese
1 tsp salt
2 1/2 cups cooked spinach (remove excess water)
6 tablespoons milk
3/4 cup sliced mushrooms

1. Beat 2 eggs, add rice, 1/2 cheese, salt and mix. Press this mixture into 9" pie plate to form a crust.

2. Beat the remaining eggs, stir in spinach, cheese, milk & mushrooms. Pour over the crust in the pie plate.

3. Bake in oven at 375 degrees for 30 minutes.

Spinach & Mushroom Quiche (#2)

1. Saute (medium heat) in butter and olive oil:
    1 small chopped onion
    8 oz. chopped fresh mushrooms

2. Add:
    3 cups chopped fresh spinach or 1 large bag thawed
        frozen spinach (squeeze out extra water)

3. Mix together and cook on low until wilted or fresh.
Remove from burner and set aside to cool

4. In mixing bowl beat together:
    4 egg whites and 6 whole eggs

5. Add:
    8 oz. shredded cheese of your choice
    4-6 ounces non-fat ricotta cheese or tofu
    8 oz. graded parmesan, asiago or romano cheese
    Season with 1 teaspoon Cajun seasoning (I also add
crushed hot red pepper), basil, oregano and other seasonings (even nutmeg!) Can add dried red bell pepper or other
dried veggies for added flavor.

6. Add sauteed vegetables.

7. If mixture is too dry can add a few tablespoons half and
half or milk

8. Pour into 8x10 greased baking dish. Cover with foil.

9. Bake at 350 for about 45 minutes. Remove cover and
bake for another 10 minutes until top is slightly browned

Serve with fresh salsa and/or sour cream and fresh Ezekiel
bread - excellent anytime of day!

Poached Huevos Rancheros

4 free range chicken eggs
Olive oil
1 can of organic black beans, drained (or about 2
    cups pre-cooked black beans)
1 small onion, minced
2-3 cloves of garlic, chopped
2 teaspoons ground cumin
1 1/2 tablespoons red chili powder
2 tablespoons chopped fresh cilantro
Sea salt and black pepper to taste
Cayenne pepper to taste
Salsa
2 large organic tortillas
Optional:
    1/2 cup shredded natural white cheddar cheese
    1-2 cups shredded romaine lettuce
    1 large avocado, cubed

1. Warm tortillas in oven (350 degrees) - wrap in foil if you want them soft/don't wrap if you want them toasted.

2. Poach eggs.

3. In a separate non-stick skillet heat olive oil, onion and garlic over medium heat for about 5 minutes stirring frequently, until translucent. Add beans and seasoning.

4. Cook beans for about 10 minutes on medium low heat, stirring occasionally. Add cilantro, salt and pepper.

5. Place a warmed tortilla over each plate. Place a spoonful of beans on each tortilla.

6. Remove eggs, and place eggs over beans. Serve with salsa, shredded cheese, romaine lettuce and avocado.

Serves 2.
Option 2: Place the beans and cheese on the tortillas and heat them in the oven while the eggs poach.

Eggs Benedict Florentine

Enjoy this version of the classic egg dish on a bed of seasoned spinach for an easy breakfast, lunch or brunch!

1 tsp organic butter
3 medium green onions, sliced
6 oz turkey ham (I actually skip this ingredient)
2 10 oz bags baby spinach or about 1-2 large
    fresh bundles - chopped (It shrinks a lot!)
1 large whole egg, divided
2 tablespoons organic butter
1-1/2 teaspoon fresh lemon, juice
4 large eggs

Spinach

1. Preheat oven to 375°F. In large skillet or ovenproof ceramic casserole over medium high, sauté scallions in oil for 1-2 minutes. Add chopped turkey ham or bacon and sauté 2 or 3 minutes longer, until meat starts to crisp and/or brown.

2. Add spinach to pan and stir-sauté until it starts to wilt. Season with salt and pepper. Remove from heat. Transfer spinach to pie plate or ovenware, if applicable. Cover and place in oven.

Hollandaise

1. Melt butter with lemon in small saucepan over medium low heat. Separate the egg, saving white to add to the 4 whole eggs.

2. Beat egg yolk with 1/2 teaspoon water, just to blend in small cup or custard cup. Stir in a little of the hot butter, stirring with a wire whisk to blend and "temper" or elevate temperature of egg yolks. Blend yolks, stirring constantly, with the rest of the lemon butter to make a smooth sauce. Put pan off and on burner, three or four times, to avoid over cooking. When thick, remove from heat.

Eggs and Assembly

1. Take casserole with spinach out of oven. Remove cover and make 4 "little nests" or indentations for the eggs. Break the four eggs and drop 1 into each nest. Add the remaining egg white.

2. Replace cover and return to oven for 4-5 minutes, just until whites start to firm. Remove from oven, remove cover and pour or spoon warm hollandaise over top of eggs. Replace cover.

3. Serve on toasted slice of Ezekiel Bread or toasted whole wheat English muffins.

Serves 4
Preparation time: 15 minutes

A KEY TO HEALTHY EATING...

Healthy Fats

The best fats to use for cooking and baking are **organic extra virgin olive oil** and **organic butter.** If you mix 1 cup olive oil and 1 cup room temperature butter in your mixer, you will have a delicious spreadable "butter" with only half the cholesterol of butter. Store in the refrigerator in a covered glass container. Use it for cooking and at the table!

Flax seed oil is also an excellent healthy fat - rich in Omega-3 fatty acids, but don't cook with it, the heat will ruin it - and keep the bottle in the fridge.

Quiche in Bell Peppers

4 red, yellow OR green bell peppers
1 cup broccoli florets,
4 EGGS
1/2 cup milk
1/2 tsp. garlic powder
crushed red pepper
1/4 tsp. dried Italian seasoning
Parmesan Cheese

1. HEAT oven to 325°F. CUT about 1/2 inch off tops of peppers; remove seeds. PLACE peppers upright in custard cups;
place cups in baking pan.

2. SPOON 1/4 cup broccoli into each pepper. BEAT eggs, milk,
garlic powder and Italian seasoning in medium bowl until
blended. POUR evenly over broccoli.

3. BAKE in center of 325°F oven until knife inserted near center comes out clean, about 60 minutes. LET STAND 5 minutes.

Cook Slow and Low.

That is, cook food slowly at lower temper-
atures to preserve all of the nutrients.
Saute on low.... use the crockpot
whenever possible.

Breakfast Cookies
(Perfect to eat on the way to work or school or for later as a snack)

2/3 cup apple sauce
1/2 cup brown sugar
1 egg
1 mashed banana
1 teaspoon almond extract
1 1/4 cups whole grain flour (wheat, barley and rye)
1/2 cup ground flax seeds
1 tsp salt
1/2 tsp baking soda
1/2 tsp nutmeg
1 tsp cinnamon
1 1/2 cup raw oatmeal - old fashioned rolled oats
3/4 cup almonds, chopped
1/4 cup raisins - optional

Directions

Preheat oven to 400 F.

Grease pan with butter - no fat in cookies makes them prone to sticking.

Sift together flour, salt, soda and spices, set aside.

In large bowl, mash banana, and add apple sauce, sugar, egg and beat until smooth.

Add extract.

Gradually stir in flour mixture and oats until well combined. Stir in nuts and raisins.

Bake 12-15 minutes (until golden brown)

Number of Servings: about 16

Oatmeal Pancakes

   1 cup old fashioned oats
   1 cup steel cut oats
   2 cups buttermilk, plain kefir or whey
Let these ingredients soak for 4 hours or overnight:

Then add:
   1/8 cup maple syrup
   1/4 cup honey
   2 eggs
   1 cup whole wheat flour (approximate)
   1/2 teaspoon baking soda
   1 1/2 teaspoons baking powder
   1/2 teaspoons salt
   1/4 cup freshly ground flax seed
   1 teaspoon cinnamon
   1 cup fresh or frozen berries
   1/2 cup walnuts (optional)
Pour batter onto hot pancake griddle - about 375 degrees
Cook for a few minutes and turn over. Cook until done.
Should make about 10 or 12 large pancakes

Top with more berries and serve with chokecherry or maple
syrup

Cranberry Pancakes

6 eggs (separated)
2 cups ricotta cheese (I use non-fat)]
2 cups cranberries (can't be too generous here!)
2 cups flour (I use 1 cup oat flour and 1 cup thick rolled
    oats)
1 teaspoon powdered stevia
2 teaspoon baking powder
1/2 cup rice milk or raw milk
2 teaspoon vanilla
Cinnamon and nutmeg

1. Beat egg whites until stiff and set aside. Mix other ingredients and then fold in egg whites,

2. Cook on hot griddle until golden on each side.

I serve with warm cranberry/raspberry sauce or choke-cherry syrup, but REAL maple syrup is also yummy.

Left overs can be refrigerated and reheated in the toaster.

Butter and honey shall he eat, that he may know to refuse the evil, and choose the good. Isaiah 7:15

Beth's Anti-cholesterol Muffins
(Plain, raisin, apple or orange)

    1 1/2 cups old fashioned oats
    1/4 cup steel cut oats
    1/8 cup flax seeds (whole)
    2 cups fat free buttermilk
Let these ingredients soak for 1-2 hours:

Add:
    1/2 cup brown sugar (can also use honey or 1/4
    cup brown sugar and 1/4 cup honey)
    2-3 tablespoons applesauce (optional)
    2 eggs or 3 egg whites
    1 cup whole wheat flour (approximate) or 1/2 cup
        amaranth
    1/2 teaspoon baking soda
    1.5 teaspoons baking powder
    1/2 teaspoons salt
    1/4 cup freshly ground flax seed
Options to add:
    Cinnamon (1 teaspoon)
    Cardamom (1/2 teaspoon)
    Raisins
    Chopped apple
    Grated orange peel plus 2 teaspoons frozen orange
        juice concentrate

Pour into and bake in muffin tins in 400 degree oven for 20 minutes.
Should make about 12 or 14

Zucchini Oatmeal Muffins

Blend till fluffy:
    3 eggs + 2 egg whites
Add: 1/4 cup olive oil
    1/4 cup honey
    3 teaspoons stevia
    2 1/2 cups rice or wheat or oat flour
    1 tablespoon baking powder
    1 teaspoon salt
    1/2 teaspoon baking soda
    1 teaspoon cinnamon/1 teaspoon cardamom
    1/4 cup ground flax seeds
    1 cup raw steel cut oats (soaked in whey for 6 hours)
    2-3 cups shredded zucchini (or ground carrots)

Stir together and pour into baking cups. Bake at 390 degrees for 20 minutes. Makes about 14.

Pumpkin Bread

Beat together:
    1 cup sugar
    1/2 cup softened butter
    4 eggs
    1/2 teaspoon cloves
    1 teaspoon cinnamon
Add: 15 oz. canned or pureed pumpkin
    2 teaspoon soda
    1 teaspoon baking powder
    1/2 teaspoon salt
    1/2 cup ground flax seeds
    1 cup whole wheat flour and 1 cup amaranth flour
    2/3 cup raisins

Pour into bread pans. Makes 2 loaves
Bake at 350 for about 1 hour - check with toothpick.

5-Grain Crockpot Breakfast

3 tablespoons bulgur (or wheat berries), uncooked
3 tablespoons brown rice, uncooked
3 tablespoons barley, uncooked
3 tablespoons millet, uncooked
1/4 cup steel cut oats
3/4 cup chopped dried mixed fruit
2 teaspoons cinnamon
3 cups water
1 tablespoons vanilla

Combine grains, dried fruit and cinnamon in crock pot. Mix well. Stir in water and vanilla. Cover on low 7 to 8 hours. Stir before serving. Add more water if desired. Serve hot, topped with plain yogurt or drizzled with maple syrup or stevia. Adding freshly ground flax seed (about 1-2 tablespoons per serving) before eating makes it 6 grain!)

A KEY TO HEALTHY EATING...

Avoid Man-Made Fats

The worst fats to use are the man-made "fake" fats. These dangerous fats include **Margarine, Crisco and Canola Oil!** These (in spite of their "healthy-marketing gimmicks) actually increase your cholesterol levels and plaque, increase insulin resistance increasing risk of diabetes and create deficiencies of the fat-soluble vitamins such as A, D, E and CoQ10!

Old Fashioned Crockpot Portage!

1 cup steal cut oats
1/2 cup chopped dried fruit (apples, raisins,
    cranberries, etc.)
2 teaspoons cinnamon
3 cups water
1 tablespoon vanilla

Combine oats, dried fruit and cinnamon in crock pot. Mix
well. Stir in water and vanilla. Cover and cook 7 - 8 hours on
low. Stir before serving, add more water if desired. Serve hot,
topped with a hefty tablespoon of plain yogurt or drizzled with
maple syrup (or stevia). Also can add freshly ground flax
seed (about 1-2 tablespoons per serving) before eating!

Cinnamon Scones
A low glycemic treat - and with cinnamon!

2 cups whole wheat flour
1-1/2 teaspoons ground cinnamon
3/4 teaspoon baking powder
1/2 teaspoon sea salt
1 teaspoon stevia
3 tablespoons butter, softened
1 large egg
1/4 cup heavy cream
3 tablespoons water

Preheat the oven to 400 F. In a medium bowl, mix together
the dry ingredients. Cut the butter into the mixture using a
pastry cutter until it forms coarse crumbles. Do not stir. In a
cup or small bowl, mix together the egg with the heavy cream
and water until the egg is completely blended. Make a well in
the center of the dry ingredients. Pour the egg mixture in and
stir together just until blended. Do not over-stir. Drop the batter by about 1/4 cup portions onto a greased baking sheet,
about 1-inch apart. Bake 12 - 15 minutes, until golden brown.
Remove from the baking sheet and serve hot. Makes 6.

SMOOTHIES

Excellent for breakfast when ground flax and Greek yogurt are added to fill you up and maintain healthy blood sugars!

Note: Greek yogurt has double the protein of regular yogurt which helps you feel full and balance blood sugar levels.

Berry Berry Smoothie

 1/2 cup frozen raspberries
 1/2 cup fresh or frozen strawberries
 1/4 cup cranberries (or other fresh fruit -
     blueberries, peaches, chopped apple, etc.)
 3/4 cup berry juice (more for thinner consistency)
 1/2 cup plain Greek yogurt
 1/8 cup (heaping) ground flax seeds
 Optional: a few ounces of sparkling mineral water
Mix together in blender. Makes about 2 servings.

Orange Dream Smoothie

 1 peach or nectarine or mango
 3/4 cup orange juice (more for thinner consistency)
 1/2 cup plain Greek yogurt
 A few drops of vanilla extract
 A drop of orange essential oil (optional)
 1/8 cup (heaping) ground flax seeds
 A few ice cubes
Mix together in blender. Makes about 2 servings.

Green Detox Smoothie

1/2 avocado
Handful or two of fresh spinach
Mint, cilantro, and parsley
1/4 cup lime juice
Plain Greek yogurt
Lemon or plain stevia to taste
Drop of lemon essential oil (optional)
Apple or melon - optional
1 tablespoon ground flax
Few ice cubes
1/2 cup water

Mix together in blender. Makes about 2 servings.

Apricot Smoothie

1/2 cup orange juice
1/2 cup plain Greek yogurt
1/2 cup peeled, pitted, chopped fresh apricots
1/8 cup (heaping) ground flax seeds

Mix together in blender. Makes about 2 servings.

Strawberry Banana Smoothie

1 cup fresh or frozen strawberries
1 banana (a little green is good or it gets too sweet)
3/4 cup apple or white grape juice
1/2 cup plain Greek yogurt
1/8 cup (heaping) ground flax seeds
Optional: Strawberry favored Emergen-C

Mix together in blender. Makes about 2 servings.

Mango, Yogurt & Lime

1 mango
1/2 cup plain Greek yogurt
1/8 cup lime juice conc. or flesh of a fresh lime
1/8 cup (heaping) ground flax seeds
Mix together in blender. Makes about 2 servings.

Cantaloupe Smoothie

1/2 cup orange juice
1/2 cup peeled, seeded and cubed cantaloupe
1/2 cup plain Greek yogurt
Honey or stevia to taste
1/2 cup ice
1/8 cup (heaping) ground flax seeds
Mix together in blender. Makes about 2 servings.

Other Ideas:

Kiwi & Strawberry

Coco powder & Banana (sweeten with stevia)

Coco powder & Almond slivers (sweeten with stevia)

SALADS

Orange-Jicama Salad
This colorful salad uses jicama, a crunchy and sweet root vegetable common to Latin countries.

    4 cups jicama, peeled and julienned
    2 oranges, sectioned and cut in half (could also use
    a can or two of mandarin oranges)
    2 tablespoons fresh cilantro, chopped
    1/2 cup crumbled feta cheese (I use fat-free)
    1/3 cup fresh orange juice
    2 tablespoons balsamic vinegar
    1 tablespoon extra-virgin olive oil
    Salt and black pepper to taste

1. Mix the jicama, orange sections, and chopped cilantro in a bowl.

2. Whisk together the remaining ingredients, toss with the jicama-orange mixture, season to taste with salt and pepper, and serve. Serves 4

Ginni's Fruit Salad
(From Ginni Crosslin, slightly modified)

In 2 1/2 quart serving bowl, layer about 2 cups of each fruit:
    Blueberries, Strawberries (cut up), Peach or Nectarine (sliced), Blackberries or raspberries
    1/4 cup coconut (optional)

In mixing bowl blend:
    8 ounces cream cheese, softened
    2 tablespoons lemon juice
    Rind of one lemon
Then fold in 1/2 cup whipping cream, whipped till stiff peaks form, sweetened with 1 teaspoon stevia. Spread cream cheese mixture over top of fruit. Chill. Serves 8.

Dr. Beth's Fruit Salad

In large glass serving bowl, layer each fruit: About 7-8 cups total:

> Blueberries, strawberries (cut up), pineapple (cut up) raspberries, apple, etc.
> Chop about 8-10 fresh mint leaves and mix into fruit.

Mix:

> 8 ounces kefir cheese, softened
> 2 tablespoons lemon juice
> Rind of one lemon
> Sweeten with 1 teaspoon liquid stevia. (plain or lemon flavor)
> Optional: 1 toothpick of lemon essential oil
> Spread Kefir cheese mixture over top of fruit. Chill.

Broccoli Salad

> 6 cups chopped broccoli
> 1/4 cup finely chopped red onion
> 3/4 cup sweetened dried cranberries or raisins
> 1/2 cup pumpkin or sunflower seeds or chopped walnuts
> 1/8 cup flax seeds - coarsely ground

Dressing:

> 3/4 cup mayonnaise
> 2 tablespoon raspberry vinegar

1. In a large bowl, place broccoli, onion, cranberries, pumpkin seeds, and flax seed.

2. In another bowl, combine mayonnaise, vinegar and sugar. Mix well.

3. Pour dressing over salad. Toss well. Chill before serving. Serves 6

Garlic Coleslaw

1 small head cabbage, shredded
1/3 of a red bell pepper, shredded
2-3 cloves garlic, minced
1 teaspoon horseradish
1/2 cup sour cream or plain yogurt
1/4 cup apple cider vinegar
1/2 teaspoon sea salt
1 tsp honey (stevia also works)
Fresh ground black pepper to taste (optional)

1. Combine ingredients in glass, stainless steel or ceramic bowl that had a lid.

2. Toss until well mixed. Adjust quantities according to taste.

3. Let flavors marinate in refrigerator for at least 4 hours. It's even better on the second day. Store cold and well sealed.

Michael's Favorite Coleslaw

1 small head green cabbage, shredded
about 1 cup red cabbage, shredded
2-3 medium sized carrots, shredded
2/3 cup homemade or olive oil mayonnaise
1/8 cup apple cider vinegar
1/2 teaspoon sea salt
1-2 tablespoons honey
Fresh ground black pepper to taste (optional)

1. Combine dressing ingredients in processor.

2. Pour dressing on shredded vegetables and toss until well mixed. Adjust quantities according to taste.

3. Let flavors marinate in refrigerator for at least 2 hours.

Grilled Romaine

2 small heads romaine, cut in 1/2 the long way, leave
   stem intact to hold leaves together.
1 clove garlic, minced
1 tablespoon olive oil
1 tablespoon balsamic vinegar
sea salt
freshly ground black pepper
Italian seasoning

1. Mix dressing ingredients together in bowl.

2. Place romaine cut side up in flat dish (like a 9 x 13 glass
baking dish). Pour dressing over halves and marinate in
refrigerator for at least 30 minutes.

3. Place romaine halves on hot grill for about 2 minutes. An
indoor grill works great because you can just close the lid
and you don't have to flip them. Serve immediately.

Barley Vegetable Salad

This summer salad combines barley, a great-tasting grain, with fresh vegetables, mint, parsley, garlic and lemon, it might remind you of a Middle Eastern dish. Barley is a very low glycemic-index grain so is excellent for diabetics! Parsley has carminative (intestinal gas-relieving) and diuretic properties.

3 cups vegetable stock or water
1 cup pearl barley
Salt to taste
1/2 cup chopped fresh parsley
1 bunch scallions or green onions, sliced thin
1 bunch radishes, sliced
1 cucumber, peeled, seeded and diced
1 red bell pepper, seeded and sliced
1/2 cup chopped fresh mint (or 1/4 cup dried mint)

Dressing:
3 tablespoons extra-virgin olive oil
3 tablespoons fresh lemon juice
4 cloves garlic, mashed
Sea salt to taste

1. Bring to a boil the vegetable stock (or water). Add barley and salt. Cover, reduce heat, and simmer until barley is tender and liquid is absorbed, about 45 minutes. Drain well and place in a medium bowl.

2. Mix the dressing together and pour over barley.

3. Allow barley to cool, then add the parsley, scallions, radishes, cucumber, red pepper and mint.

4. Mix well and chill for several hours before serving.

Wheat Berry Salad

2/3 cups hard wheat berries (red or white)
3/4 cup chopped walnuts
2 stalks celery, finely chopped
1/2 cup tart dried cherries, chopped
1 bunch scallions (green onion), white and green parts, chopped
1/2 cup finely chopped parsley leaves (best added right before serving)
4 tablespoons extra virgin olive oil
3 tablespoons lemon juice
2 tablespoons apple cider vinegar
Sea salt
Freshly ground black pepper

1. In a large pot combine the wheat berries and enough water to come 2 inches over the wheat berries. Bring to a boil and cook uncovered for 1 hour, or until tender. Drain and let cool.

2.Toast the walnuts in a medium dry skillet over medium-high heat until fragrant, 2 to 3 minutes.

3. In a large bowl, combine the wheat berries, walnuts, celery, dried cherries, scallions, parsley, olive oil and lemon juice. Season, to taste, with sea salt and pepper.

This salad is adequate for a main dish for lunch or dinner, but is a good side dish, too. It can be served cold or at room temperature.

NOTE: This salad can also be made with __cooked__ __wild__ __rice__ instead of wheat berries! Try adding some chopped fresh sage. This is awesome with lemon chicken!!

Roasted Beet & Arugula Salad

Roasting beets intensifies their sweetness. The sweetness of the beets, the licorice-like flavor of the fennel, and the slight bitterness of the arugula make for a salad full of wonderfully contrasting flavors. If your beets come topped with greens that are small and tender, use them in place of the arugula.

2 pounds beets
1 pound small red-skinned potatoes
1/3 cup balsamic vinegar
1 tablespoon olive oil
2 tablespoons prepared horseradish, drained
3/4 teaspoon sea salt
1 bulb fennel, trimmed, quartered lengthwise, and
    thinly sliced (2-1/2 cups)
2 scallions, thinly sliced
2 bunches arugula (3 cups)
6 ounces soft goat cheese, crumbled

1. Preheat oven to 400°F. If beets are small, wrap several together in foil. If large, wrap each one separately. Place on baking sheet; bake 1 hour or until packet feels soft when pressed. (Timing may vary depending upon size and age of beets). When cool enough to handle, slip skins off beets (if you don't want to stain your hands, hold beets with paper towel). Cut beets into 1/2-inch wedges.

2. Meanwhile, in large pot of boiling water, cook potatoes for 20 minutes or until tender. When cool enough to handle, cut into 1/2-inch chunks.

3. In large bowl, whisk together vinegar, oil, horseradish, and salt. Add fennel, scallions, arugula, beets, and potatoes; toss to combine. Serve salads with goat cheese scattered on top.

Orange Wild Rice Salad

1. Combine:
   2 cups cooked wild rice, chilled
   1 cup orange sections, sliced into 3 or more pieces
   1/2 cup diced celery
   1/2 cup dried cranberries or cherries, chopped

2. Mix together dressing:
   1/4 cup thawed organic frozen orange juice conc.
   2 tablespoons lemon juice concentrate
   1 tablespoon dijon mustard
   1 1/2 teaspoons extra virgin olive oil
   salt and pepper to taste

3. Pour dressing over rice mixture and chill.

Blood Orange Salad w/ Green Onions

   5 blood oranges (or navels will work too)
   2 green onions, chopped
   3 tablespoons fresh parsley, chopped
   Crushed red pepper, 1/2 teaspoon or more to taste
   1-2 tablespoons olive oil

Peel oranges and divide sections. Cut then into 1/2 inch
pieces. Place in glass bowl and add other ingredients. Toss
gently to combine.

Mustard Chicken and Arugula Salad

6 oz. skinless, boneless chicken breast
1/2 teaspoons sea salt
1/8 teaspoons black pepper
2 tablespoons dijon mustard
1 teaspoons olive oil
3 cups arugula, washed and dried
2 tablespoons chopped walnuts
Dressing:
1 tablespoon honey + 1 tablespoon dijon mustard

1. Season chicken with salt and pepper. Coat with Dijon mustard and 1 tablespoon of honey-dijon dressing. Refrigerate 30 minutes or overnight.

2. Preheat oven to 375 degrees.

3. Heat 8" ovenproof nonstick skillet over medium heat until hot. Add oil and chicken. Cook 3 minutes on one side, turn over and cook 1 more minute. Transfer the skillet to oven until chicken is cooked through, about 8-10 minutes.

4. Transfer chicken to plate. Slice into thin strips.

5. In a large bowl, toss arugula and remaining honey-dijon dressing. Mound arugula on two plates and top with sliced chicken and walnuts.

Serves 2

Red Cabbage and Apple Salad

1/2 medium-sized head of red cabbage, chopped
2 red apples, chopped
1/2 cup dried cranberries
1 teaspoon cinnamon
1/4 cup chopped walnuts or slivered almonds
1/2 - 2/4 cup organic berry juice, unsweetened

Mix and marinate in refrigerator for at least 2 hours or overnight.

Asparagus Avocado Salad

1 pound fresh asparagus, trimmed and cut into 1 1/2
    inch pieces
8 medium fresh mushrooms, sliced
1 large ripe avocado, peeled and cubed
1 medium zucchini, diced
1 large tomato, seeded and chopped
1 medium red onion, sliced
2 tablespoons lemon juice, fresh
2 tablespoons olive oil
1 tablespoons balsamic vinegar
1 teaspoons dijon mustard
1 garlic clove, chopped
1/2 teaspoons dried basil
1/2 teaspoons dried thyme
1/4 teaspoons sea salt

1. Steam asparagus. Drain and cool.

2. In a large bowl, combine asparagus and the next 5 ingredients; toss gently.

3. In a jar, mix all the other ingredients and shake well. Pour over salad, toss gently and serve. Can be refrigerated.

Serves 7

Avocado Salad

1-2 large ripe avocados, peeled and cubed
2 large tomatoes, chopped
1/4 medium red onion, sliced thin
1/3 cup red bell pepper, chopped
1/2 cup feta cheese, crumbled
Dressing:
2 gloves garlic, chopped
3 tablespoons lemon juice, fresh
2 tablespoons olive oil
1/4 cup fresh cilantro, chopped

Combine first 5 ingredients in large bowl. Mix dressing and pour over salad. Let marinate for a couple of hours in fridge before serving.

Serves 3-4

Salmon Caesar Salad

1/2 head romaine lettuce, torn or lightly chopped
1/4 cup parmesan cheese
1 small yellow, red, and/or green sweet pepper, cut into matchstick-size strips
1/4 cup sliced pitted ripe olives
6 ounces smoked salmon, skinned, boned, and broken into chunks; or 3 to 4 ounces thinly sliced, smoked salmon (lox-style), cut into bite-size strips; or 4 ounces grilled salmon, skinned, boned, and broken into chunks.
Caesar dressing on page 104.

In a large salad bowl combine lettuce, cheese, sweet pepper strips, and olives; toss gently to coat. Add salmon and the dressing; toss before serving.

Serves 3

Broccoli Salad with Oranges

Broccoli is excellent for regulating blood sugar. This is an easy to make, simple, colorful and refreshing salad, sweetened with oranges.

    whole stalk broccoli
    1/2 cup red onion, finely diced
    1 small can mandarin oranges, drained

Salad dressing:
    1A few drops of the liquid stevia extract
    1/3 cup olive oil
    2 teaspoon finely grated fresh orange peel
    juice of 1 orange
    1 tablespoon apple cider vinegar

Remove flowerettes from the head of the broccoli; wash and drain. Cut into small, bite-sized flowerettes. Place in large bowl.

Clean and peel stem of broccoli. Cut into 1- inch chunks. Place in processor and chop until evenly chopped - about pea-sized. Add to bowl. Add diced onion.

In small bowl, wisk together dressing ingredients. Pour over broccoli mixture and toss together. Refrigerate.

Serves 4-5

Easy Spinach Mushroom Salad

Baby spinach leaves for two servings.
White button mushrooms. sliced
Red onion, slivered thin

1. In serving bowl wisk dressing ingredients:
1 tablespoon extra virgin olive oil
1 tablespoon balsamic or apple cider vinegar
1/2 tablespoon dijon mustard

2. After wisking, add button mushrooms, toss and let marinate for 20-30 minutes. Then add spinach, slivered onions and toss again. Finish with sea salt and black pepper to taste.

Spinach Orange Salad

6 cups torn fresh spinach
2 medium oranges, peeled and sectioned
1 small red onion, sliced thin
1/2 cup sliced water chestnuts, drained
Freshly ground black pepper
2 tablespoons orange juice
1 tablespoon extra virgin olive oil
1 teaspoon dijon mustard
1 tablespoon honey
1 teaspoon toasted sesame seed or slivered almonds

1. In a large salad bowl place spinach, orange sections, onion rings, water chestnuts and almonds. Add black pepper.

2. For dressing,in glass measuring cup wisk orange juice, oil, honey, sesame seed and mustard. Pour dressing over salad. Toss lightly to coat. Serve immediately. Makes 4 servings.

Red Potato Salad

1 1/2 pounds red potatoes, organic if possible
6 hard boiled eggs peeled and chopped
1/4 cup dijon or Dusseldorf mustard
1/4 cup dry white wine
1/4 cup white wine vinegar
2 tablespoons extra-virgin olive oil
1 yellow onion, chopped fine
2 stalks celery, chopped
2 teaspoons capers
1/2 cup chopped fresh parsley
Chopped fresh dill to taste

1. Boil potatoes in their skins, covered, just until they can be easily pierced with a sharp knife.

2. Meanwhile, prepare dressing in a jar, combining mustard, wine, vinegar, olive oil, salt and pepper to taste; shake well.

3. Drain potatoes, let cool enough to handle, then peel and cut into thick slices. Place in a large bowl.

4. Pour dressing over the potatoes while warm, toss well.

5. Add eggs, chopped onion, sliced celery, capers, parsley, dill and other vegetables (red bell pepper, radish, etc.).

6. Correct seasoning. Chill until served.

Quick and Easy Dressing

3 tablespoons of extra virgin olive oil
3 teaspoons of balsamic vinegar or lemon juice
1 teaspoon of raw, unheated honey
1 teaspoon of mustard

Use a fork to wisk all ingredients together in a small bowl.
Pour over a vegetable salad. Toss to evenly coat.

Caesar

1/3 cup Olive oil
1/4 cup balsamic vinegar
1 tablespoons stone ground or dijon mustard
1 tablespoons fresh chopped garlic
1 tablespoons parmesan cheese

Buttermilk Dressing

2/3 cup low-fat buttermilk
2 teaspoon dijon mustard
2 tablespoons grated cucumber
1 green onion, thinly sliced
1 tablespoons chopped fresh parsley
 Salt and pepper, to taste

Raspberry-Orange Vinaigrette

1/4 cup orange marmalade
1/4 cup raspberry vinegar
1 tablespoons flax or olive oil
2 tablespoons chopped fresh cilantro

Mayonnaise

(from Sally Fallons' "Nourishing Traditions")

1 whole egg plus one yolk (room temperature)
1 tablespoon whey
2 teaspoons dijon mustard
Sea salt
1 1/2 tablespoons lemon juice
1 3/4 cups extra virgin olive oil

Place first 5 ingredients in processor and mix. Then while mixing, slowly pour in oil. Let stand at room temperature for 7 hours or if your home is cool, in a warmed oven. (Heat to approximately110 degrees, turn off oven and turn on light and keep door closed). Cultures in the whey ferment for a wonderful flavor! This will keep in the refrigerator for several months and will become firmer with time.

If you do not have whey you can make the mayonaise without it, but you will need to use it all right away as it will not keep.

So where do you get whey?

It's the pale yellowish watery stuff that floats to the top of yogurt - it's always best to buy organic (plain) or make your own from raw milk. Don't throw the whey out - it contains valuable cultures and nutrients. It will keep in a mason jar in your refrigerator for months!

Whey can be used as a starter culture for fermented vegetables (like sauerkraut), for soaking grains and as a starter for many beverages. Use it to soak your oats and other grains, freshly ground flour etc. to make bread, muffins, pancakes, etc.

Traditionally, a small amount of whey was consumed with each meal to aid with digestive problems!

SPINACH, BEETS AND OTHER VEGETABLES

Spinach is exceptionally rich in carotenoids, including beta-carotene and lutein, and also contains quercetin, a phyto-chemical with antioxidant and bone-protective properties. Spinach is rich in vitamins and minerals, particularly folate (folic acid), which lowers homocysteine which is associated with heart disease risk, vitamin K, magnesium, and manganese; it also contains more protein than most vegetables. (Although the protein is incomplete--are low in the amino acid methionine--it is complemented by the protein in rice and other grains.)

Raw spinach is a healthy addition to salads, but to get the **full benefit** from spinach, eat it cooked at least some of the time. Cooking increases the antioxidant carotenoids and inactivates the oxalates which inhibit calcium absorption.

Sauteéd Spinach

This is spinach with a "Greek" flair (because of the feta). It is easy to make as an everyday vegetable on its own, or as a side dish for grilled salmon or chicken.

- 1 tablespoons olive oil
- 1/2 small red onion, thinly sliced into rings
- 4-6 cloves fresh garlic, sliced
- 2 lbs fresh baby spinach or swiss chard washed and de-stemmed (if frozen, thaw drain excess water)
- 1/2 teaspoon grated lemon peel
- 1/4 cup feta cheese, crumbled (optional)
- Sea salt and freshly ground black pepper to taste

1. Sauté onion and garlic until onions start to wilt. Add spinach and quickly sauté for 2-3 minutes. Add lemon peel, salt and pepper. Cook a few seconds more to release flavors.

2.. Add crumbled feta cheese and stir to incorporate. Transfer to serving dish and serve immediately.

Serves 4 Preparation time: 10 minutes

Creamed Spinach

  2 tablespoons butter
  1 tablespoon olive oil
  1 Vidalia onion, minced
  2 cloves garlic, minced
  2 bunches spinach, stemmed and chopped
  Salt and freshly ground black pepper
  1/4 teaspoon freshly ground nutmeg
  1/4 cup heavy cream

1. In a medium saute pan over medium heat, melt butter and olive oil.

2. Mix in the onions and garlic; cook for several minutes until soft.

3. Add the chopped spinach and warm through. Add the salt, nutmeg and the heavy cream. Mix well.

4. Cook until liquid reduces by half, roughly 3 to 4 minutes.

Spinach Wild Rice Casserole

2 cups wild rice (I sometimes mix in some other
    kinds of brown rice too)
4 cups chicken stock

Saute in 1 tablespoon butter:
    1/3 cup chopped onion or green onion
    4-5 cloves chopped/minced garlic
When done, add juice of 1/2 lemon and remove from heat.

Mix together:
    1/2 cup ricotta or cottage cheese (I often use fat free)
    3/4 cup sour cream (I used low fat)
    8 oz parmesan (about 1 cup - save some for top)
      (I also add some grated swiss on top)
    1 egg
    1 teaspoon garlic salt
    1 tablespoon soy sauce
    juice of rest of lemon
    dash of nutmeg

Add onions, garlic and 8 oz package of frozen chopped
spinach - thawed.

Mix with cooked rice. Top with additional parmesan cheese
and a few sprinkles of cayenne pepper.

Bake covered (355 degrees) for 20-25 minutes - last few
minutes uncover and broil till the top is browned.

Spinach Pie (Spanakopita)

Based on the traditional Greek dish spanakopita, this interpretation will make a spinach lover out of anyone. Make sure that the spinach is washed very well, or use two 10-ounce packages of frozen chopped spinach.

2 teaspoons olive oil
12 scallions, sliced
4-6 cloves garlic, chopped
Two 10-ounce packages fresh spinach, cleaned, chopped
3/4 cup crumbled feta cheese
2/3 cup low-fat cottage cheese or ricotta
1/2 cup minced dill (optional)
2 eggs, lightly beaten
1/4 teaspoon freshly ground black pepper
6 sheets phyllo dough, thawed if frozen

1. Preheat the oven to 350F. Butter an 8" square baking pan. In a medium nonstick skillet, heat the oil. Add the scallions and garlic; cook, stirring, 1 minute. Add the spinach; cook, stirring as needed, until just wilted, 3-5 minutes. Transfer to a medium bowl; stir in the cheeses, dill, eggs and pepper.

2. Spray 1 phyllo sheet with nonstick cooking spray; top with another sheet and spray it. Line the baking pan with these 2 sheets, letting the edges hang over the sides. Spread the spinach mixture over the phyllo. Cover the filling with the remaining 4 sheets, spraying each sheet and tucking them into the pan. Fold in the outside sheets.

3. Bake until golden, 30-35 minutes.
Serves 4

Indian Creamed Curried Spinach with Sag Paneer

1/2 cup water
1 lb. fresh spinach, washed, de-stemmed, chopped
3 tablespoons ghee or butter
1 tablespoon finely chopped ginger
1/2 cup finely chopped onion
1 teaspoon salt
1/4 teaspoon ground cumin
1/4 teaspoon turmeric
1/2 teaspoon ground coriander
1/2 teaspoon garam masala
1 cup cheese (paneer), cut into 1-inch cubes

1. Combine 1/2 of the water and a handful of the spinach in a jar of a blender. Blend at high speed for 30 seconds. Keep adding spinach until about half is blended. Add a little more water, if necessary, to puree.

2. In a large skillet, heat the butter over moderate heat. Add the ginger and saute for one minute. Add the onions and salt and continue sauteing for 5 more minutes.

3. Stirring after each addition, add the cumin, turmeric, coriander, and garam masala. Then stir in the leafy and pureed spinach. Reduce the heat and cook the mixture uncovered, for 20 to 30 minutes. Most of the liquid should evaporate.

4. At the last minute, gently add the paneer. Serve hot with rice and or Naan (Indian flat bread).
Serves 4

Pasta w/ Spinach Pesto

8 oz. whole wheat or multi grain penne or spiral pasta
Handful or two of spinach leaves (set aside)
Combine in processor:
3 garlic cloves
4 ounces soft goat cheese (with herbs)
 3/4 teaspoon sea salt
1/2 teaspoon freshly ground black pepper
1/2 teaspoon red pepper flakes (optional)
 8 ounces fresh baby spinach leaves
 2 tablespoons Parmesan

1. While pasta is cooking, combine the remaining ingredients in processor and pulse until smooth. If needed you can add a tablespoon or two of extra virgin olive oil. Place this in a large serving bowl and place in a warm oven.

2. A minute (or less) before the pasta is done. Add the spinach leaves to the boiling water. After 30-60 seconds, drain the water from the pasta and now cooked spinach.

3. Add the cooked pasta and spinach to the spinach pesto and toss. add a few more drops of olive oil if needed. Top with some extra parmesan cheese before serving.

Swiss Chard

Swiss chard is a good source of beta-carotene, potassium, vitamin K, magnesium and dietary fiber. It's distinctive flavor is akin to (but milder than) that of beet greens. The dark green leaves are wider and flatter than beet greens, and they have a full-bodied texture similar to spinach (for which chard is a good substitute).

Steaming: Tender chard will cook quickly steamed in a vegetable steamer over boiling water. Cooking time is about five minutes - or until chard is wilted. Serve with balsamic vinegar.

It can also be added to soups or used in place of spinach in various recipes.

Beets

Beets are noted for their sweetness (they have the highest sugar content of any vegetable), but they are very low in calories. Their sweet flavor comes through whether the beets are fresh or canned. Unlike many other processed vegetables, canned beets are perfectly acceptable in both taste and texture; if not pickled, their sweet flavor is largely unaffected by the canning process.

Fresh beets, however, have twice the folate (folic acid) and potassium, and have a distinctive flavor and a crisp texture not found in canned beets. Fresh beets also supply a nutritional bonus--their green tops are an excellent source of beta-carotene, calcium and iron. Beets are rich in iron, folic acid, potassium and fiber.

The best way to cook beets is to roast them in the oven. This locks in it's nutrients and intensifies the natural sweet-

ness of beets. It's not a quick method, though: To save time, cook a large quantity of beets at once, then chill some for later use in salads. You can also bake beets when you're baking or roasting something else. Wrap beets in foil, place them in a baking pan, and bake in a 400°F oven until tender. Unwrap and let stand until they're just cool enough to handle, then peel them while still warm. Cooking time: 1 1/2 - 2 hours, depending on size.

Orange-Roasted Beets & Greens

Use the entire beet in this beautiful, healthy side dish, rich in beta-carotene, iron and folic acid.

> 4 pounds beets with tops (about 2-1/2 pounds of
>   beets weighed without the tops)
> 3/4 cup orange juice
> 3 tablespoons raspberry vinegar
> 2 tablespoons brown sugar
> 1-1/2 teaspoons fresh lemon juice
> 1/4 teaspoon caraway seeds
> Pinch of ground cloves
> Pinch of allspice
> 1/2 teaspoons cornstarch
> 2 teaspoons olive oil

1. Preheat oven to 400°F.

2. Separate tops from beets. Wash well, trim fibrous center ribs, coarsely shred, wrap in a towel and refrigerate until ready to use.

3. Wrap each beet in a double layer of foil, making sure they are well sealed. Bake for 1-1/2 to 2 hours (depending on their size), until fork-tender. Remove from oven and allow to cool.

4. Meanwhile, in small nonreactive saucepan, combine orange juice, vinegar, brown sugar, lemon juice, caraway,

cloves, and allspice. Measure out 2 tablespoons of mixture and combine in small bowl with cornstarch. Set aside.

5. Bring remaining mixture to a boil over medium-high heat and cook 1 minute. Stir cornstarch mixture into saucepan and cook until dressing begins to thicken, about 30 seconds. Remove from heat and set aside.

6. When beets are cool enough to handle, peel and cut into thin slices. Toss with dressing and let stand at room temperature at least 30 minutes to meld flavors.

7. Shortly before serving, heat oil in large nonstick skillet over medium-high heat. Add beet greens in batches and cook until wilted; adding 1 or 2 tablespoons of water if the skillet becomes dry. Serve beets on bed of the wilted greens topped with orange sauce.

A KEY TO HEALTHY COOKING...

Double the Garlic!

I have hardly found a recipe where I don't double the amount of garlic it asks for. Garlic is well established scientifically as an agent that reduces blood cholesterol and triglycerides in the blood (as much as 10-15%). It reduces blood clotting, is anti-tumor, anti-fungal, anti-bacterial and so much more! And... it tastes so good!
Isn't God awesome!

SOUPS

Sweet Potato Chowder

1 large onion, chopped
4 cloves garlic, minced
2 tablespoons olive oil
1 1/2 teaspoon curry paste (or 3 teaspoons curry
    powder)
6 medium sweet potatoes - peeled and cut into
    3/4 inch pieces (about 8 cups)
1 can organic chicken broth
1 cup water
1 14 oz. can of lite coconut milk (look in Asian food
    section of store) - (can also use 1/2 and 1/2)
1 2-inch piece of lemon grass or peel and juice of
    one large lemon
2 teaspoon grated fresh ginger (optional)
2 tablespoons maple syrup

Saute onion and garlic in oil for several minutes. Add curry paste and cook for few more minutes.

Add rest of ingredients except for ginger and maple syrup. Heat to boiling and reduce heat to simmer for about 15 minutes. Remove lemon grass.

Take out about 3/4 and puree in processor or blender till smooth. Return to stove and mix with remaining. So yummy!

Old Fashioned Potato Soup

6 cups potatoes (with skin on) cut into bite size pieces
16 ounces organic chicken broth
Enough water to (almost cover) cook potatoes - maybe
a cup.
4 stems leeks, chopped
2 cups celery, chopped
1 cup chopped natural beef bacon or sausage (optional)
- no nitrates please.
1 and 1/2 to 2 cups milk (depending how thick or thin
you like your soup)
4 ounces goat cheese with garlic and herbs
sea salt
freshly ground black pepper
Crushed red pepper (optional)
olive oil to saute vegetables.

1. Saute leeks in olive oil until carmelized. This takes a
while so don't start potatoes yet.

2. Remove from pan, set aside in bowl and start potatoes.

3. Saute celery and beef bacon

4. When potatoes are done (tender to fork), turn off heat
and uncover so some of the liquid evaporates.

5. Place a couple of ladles of cooked potatoes and broth
into food processor. Add the goat cheese and about 1/2 of
the cooked leeks. Process until smooth.

6. In a large soup kettle, add celery, meat, remaining leeks,
potatoes, broth and pureed potatoes. Add about 1 cup milk
sea salt, pepper and stir. Season to taste. Let simmer for
about 15 minutes on low, cover off. Add more milk if you
like a thinner soup.

Butternut Wild Rice Soup

1 large onion, chopped. Saute in olive oil
1 teaspoon curry paste (or 2 teaspoon curry powder)
1 large or 2 small butternut squash, cooked. (I
      puree in processor or blender with some of
      the chicken broth.)
2 cans organic chicken broth
1/2 cup water or coconut milk
1 cup cooked wild rice
2 teaspoon grated fresh ginger (optional)
2 tablespoons maple syrup
Salt and pepper to taste

I make this in the crockpot. Heat to boiling on high setting and then reduce heat setting to low to simmer for about 30 minutes.

Can add milk to thin if desired.
Can serve with sour cream. Yummy!

Red Lentil and Squash Soup

3 cups water
One can low sodium organic chicken broth
3/4 cup red lentils
1/2 cup chopped onion
1 clove chopped garlic
2 cups sliced yellow squash (raw or use leftovers)
1 cup plain yogurt
1/2 teaspoon sea salt
1/2 teaspoon nutmeg
Can add a 1/4 cup of half and half or cream for
      creamier, richer soup. (optional)
I usually add plain non-fat yogurt instead.

Simmer first 4 ingredients for about 30 minutes.
Add squash, nutmeg, salt and simmer 10 more minutes and puree all ingredients (add yogurt) in blender.
Return to saucepan and keep warm on low until serving.

Cajun Black Bean Soup

1. Presoak overnight if possible- discard water and rinse.
    16 oz. dried beans (about 2 cups)
    About 5 cups water

2. Cook beans in crockpot or stovetop with
    30 ounces organic chicken or beef broth

3. Saute in olive oil:
    4-6 cloves garlic, chopped
    1 medium-sized red onion, chopped
    Chopped peppers of any kind, jalapeno, etc.

4. Add to the beans are about 1/2 or 3/4 way done.

5. Add seasonings:
    2 teaspoons ground cumin
    2 teaspoons chili powder
    1/2 teaspoon oregano
    3/4 teaspoon salt
    1 teaspoon cayenne pepper
    1 teaspoon cajun seasoning

6. Puree beans in processor and return to cooking pot. I like to add about 1/2 cup sour cream before serving.

7. Adjust thickness of soup by adding water to desired consistency. Serve with:
    Fresh salsa (see recipe on page 89.)
    Dab of sour cream
    Half an avocado, peeled and diced (1/2 cup)
    4 lime wedges

Smoked Salmon w/ White Bean Soup

A tasty idea I discovered at King's Fish House in Laguna Hills, CA. Locations also in Long Beach and Orange, CA.

3 lbs. dry navy beans
3 lbs. pre-cooked hot-smoked salmon cut into 1/2 inch cubes
1 1/4 cups diced celery
1 1/4 cups diced carrots
1 1/4 cups diced onion
1/2 bunch chopped cilantro
8 cloves chopped garlic
4 ounces butter or olive oil
4 ounces flour
1 quart tomato sauce
2 tablespoons fresh thyme (or 1 tablespoons dried)
2 bay leaves
1 tablespoons. paprika
2 tablespoons. black pepper
Extra water if needed

1. Cook beans separately in unsalted water until al dente'. Drain water and set aside.

2. In large heavy soup kettle cook celery, carrots, onion, cilantro and garlic in butter or olive oil until vegetables are transparent. Add flour and cook until mixture starts to brown and smells nutty.

3. Add remaining ingredients except for salmon and cook about 20 minutes (until beans are tender) on medium to low heat. Add salmon. Serve when salmon is warmed through. Perfect with fresh sourdough bread (and a glass of cabernet).

Serves 16 cups or 8 bowls

Lentil Soup

16 oz. dried lentils (about 2 1/2 cups)
About 6 cups water
Add about 1/2 way through cooking:
1/2 head of garlic, chopped
Cumin, about 1 teaspoon
Sea salt
Cayenne or red pepper flakes (to taste)
1 cup chopped carrots

Cook in crockpot on low for about 6 hours OR on high for about 4 hours - stir occasionally. On stovetop, less than 2 hours. When lentils are soft stir them to mash them up a little or puree in processor. Stir in about 1 cup of plain yogurt or sour cream and serve.

"Creamy" Carrot Bisque

Most soups can be pureed to make any veggie soup seem thick and "creamy."

1 onion, chopped
2 stalks celery, chopped
5 cups carrots, cut into 1/8" rounds
4 cups pure water or veggie stock
1 teaspoon Bragg's Liquid Amino's
1/2 teaspoon dried bouquet garni
1/2 teaspoon dried basil
1 clove garlic, minced any other herbs you'd like (try curry or cumin; or for a savory soup, try tarragon or dill)

1. Place all vegetables into a large soup pot with the water or stock. Bring to a boil. Add the soy sauce and herbs. Reduce the heat, simmer covered for 10-15 minutes until the carrots are tender.

2. Puree about 1/2 of the soup in a blender or food processor.

3. Recombine the reserved carrots, broth and puree. Stir well and bring to a boil. Add any other seasonings to taste. Serve with a big side salad and warm bread.   Serves 4

Spinach Soup

3/4 gallon water or chicken broth or 1/2 and 1/2
24 ounces leaf spinach
2 lbs. skinless chicken
1 medium onion chopped
6 cloves of garlic, chopped
1 16 oz. container of french onion dip (or sour cream
    and some roasted onion powder).
1 tablespoon lemon/pepper seasoning
1 tablespoon of oregano and basil (each)
1 tablespoon parsley
1 teaspoon thyme

1. Add 1/2 of water or broth and the chicken, to pot. Cook on high to boiling, and cook, covered, for 15 minutes. Reduce heat, take chicken out of water and cut up in small pieces. Add back into pot. Throw away bones and unwanted parts.

2. Add rest of water or broth, spinach, onion, garlic, lemon/pepper seasoning, oregano, parsley, basil, and thyme. Bring back to boil. Boil for 5 minutes. Stirring every three minutes. Then adjust heat to medium heat. Cook for 15 minutes more stirring every five minutes.

3. Add french onion dip to pot, and cook for 5 minutes more, stirring often. Serve warm. Refrigerate leftovers. (Use leftover within 5 days.)

Spinach Supreme Soup

If you like spinach, you'll love this recipe. You can make it with or without the vegan sour cream. If you choose to make it with the sour cream, try it cold for lunch. Very good!

   8 cups pure water
   2 cups sliced mushrooms (reserve 1 cup)
   2 cups onion, sliced in thin half-circles
   1 1/2 cups thinly sliced celery
   2 lbs finely chopped fresh spinach (reserve half for
       later)
   1 cup diced green onions (reserve 1/4 cup for garnish)
   2 tablespoons soy sauce
   1 tablespoons each dried basil and oregano
   1/2 tsp ground celery seed
   2 teaspoon sea salt
   1/2 teaspoon cayenne pepper
   1 cup sour cream

1.In a large soup pot, bring to a boil the water, 2 cups of the mushrooms, onions, celery and 1/2 of the spinach. Reduce heat and simmer, covered, for about 20 minutes, until onions and celery are tender.

2. Add reserved mushrooms and spinach, 3/4 cup of the green onions, soy sauce and spices. Simmer about 10 minutes.

3. For the creamy soup option, turn the burner to the lowest heat. In a blender, place the sour cream and enough of the hot soup broth that the mixture will blend (about 1 cup). Blend until smooth, then add mixture back to the soup and heat very gently for a few minutes. Don't boil. Garnish with the remaining green onions.
Yields 4 quarts.

Lemon Chicken Noodle Soup
(Works better than a flu shot any day!!!)

1 large onion, chopped
8-10 garlic cloves, chopped
2-3 raw chicken breasts, cut into bite size pieces.
    (Can use dark meat if you prefer or a whole
    chicken, cooked first and de-boned)
1 1/2 cup celery, chopped
Olive oil and butter
6 cups chicken stock
1 cup lemon juice
2 cups chopped carrots
12 ounces sliced mushrooms
1 large sweet potato or yam, shredded
Cayenne pepper to taste - the more the better!
Sea salt and pepper to taste
16 oz. frozen "homemade" style egg noodles
Milk and corn starch to thicken, if desired.

1. Saute' first 4 ingredients in olive oil and butter for about 5 minutes.

2. Add the chicken stock and cook for about 15 minutes.

3. Add lemon juice, carrots, mushrooms, sweet potato, cayenne and cook for about 1/2 hour until carrots are soft.

4. Add noodles and cook until done, about 15 minutes.

5. I like to thicken the soup by adding milk and cornstarch. Place about three tablespoons corn starch in a jar, add about 1/4 cup milk. Put the lid on the jar and shake. Pour this into your bubbling soup and let it warm up to a boil again for several minutes.
Add salt and pepper to taste and serve.

Orzo, Lentil and Flax Soup

1/8 cup butter w/ splash of olive oil
1 medium onion, finely chopped
4 cloves fresh, chopped garlic
1 medium carrot, finely chopped
1 celery stalk, finely chopped
1/2 green pepper, finely chopped
5 cups boiling water
1/8 cup low sodium chicken soup base
1 bay leaf
2 teaspoon Worcestershire sauce or Bragg's Liquid
    Aminos
28 oz. of canned tomatoes with herbs and spices;
    break up tomatoes
1/3 cup orzo pasta or any small soup pasta
1/3 cup dried lentils, rinsed
1 teaspoon honey
1/4 cup ground flax

1. In a large pot, over medium to medium-low heat, melt
butter. Add onion, garlic, carrot, celery and green pepper.
Gently saute over medium-low heat for 20 minutes, stirring
occasionally.

2. Add boiling water, soup base, bay leaf, Worcestershire
sauce (or Bragg's), tomatoes with juice, orzo and lentils.
Stir.

3. Slowly simmer for 1 hour with lid ajar, stirring occasionally until lentils are soft.

4. Remove from heat. Add honey and flax seed. Stir and
serve.
Yield: 10 servings   Serving size: 1 cup

Lentil Vegetable Soup

1/2 cup celery, chopped
1/2 cup carrots, chopped
1 cup white cabbage, shredded or chopped
1 large onion, chopped
6 cloves garlic, chopped
1 tablespoon olive oil
2-3 bay leaves
7-8 cups stock or water
1 tablespoon Italian herbs
2 cups green lentils
2 red potatoes (optional)
1 bunch spinach
1 teaspoon sea salt
Cayenne pepper to taste
3 tablespoons red wine or balsamic vinegar

1. Heat the oil in a large soup pot and add the vegetables and bay leaves. Cook on medium heat until the vegetables are soft, then add the water, herbs, and lentils. Cook over medium to high heat for 45 minutes, adding more water as needed (some evaporates during cooking).

2. Chop the potatoes into small cubes, if using. Add them to the soup and cook until soft, about 10 to 12 minutes. Add the spinach leaves, and cook for about 2 more minutes, just long enough to wilt the leaves.

3. Remove from the heat. Stir in the red wine vinegar and leave covered until ready to serve. Serves about 8

A KEY TO STABLE BLOOD SUGAR LEVELS... Lentils and Beans!

The ultimate food for diabetics! Beans are low in fat, have a low glycemic index, high in complex carbohydrates, high in protein and fiber!

Spicy Bean Soup

This tasty, spicy recipe is filling, healthy and has a low glycemic index

1/4 cup dry sherry or red wine
1/3 cup chopped onion
1/4 cup chopped celery
1/4 cup diced red bell peppers
1/2 - 1 cup diced tomatoes (canned or fresh)
3 cups vegetable or chicken stock
2 cups cooked white beans (I prefer to cook my own dried beans, but if you are using canned be sure to rinse and drain them)
2 tablespoons. minced fresh parsley or cilantro
1 -5 cloves minced fresh garlic
1 teaspoon ground cumin
1/2 teaspoon ground coriander
1 teaspoon cayenne pepper or to taste
Cajun seasoning to taste

If you prefer a thicker soup, about five minutes before serving, add some arrow root powder or crushed dried bean powder - (available in the health section of your grocery store).

Heat sherry or wine in large soup pot over medium-high heat until bubbling. Add onion and cook, stirring, 3 minutes until soft but not browned. Add celery, bell peppers, tomatoes and cook 5 minutes.

Add stock, beans, parsley, garlic, cumin and coriander and bring to boil. Lower heat to medium and cook 20 minutes. Add cayenne and salt and pepper to taste. Serves about 4.

Hearty Bean And Vegetable Stew

from Chet Day *(modified)*

1 lb assorted dry beans *
2 cups vegetable or tomato juice
1/2 cup dry white wine (optional)
1/8 cup soy sauce or Bragg's liquid Amino's
1/3 cup apple juice
1 cup celery, diced
1 cup parsnips, diced
1 cup carrots, diced
1 cup mushrooms, diced
1 onion, chopped
1 teaspoon basil, dried
1 teaspoon parsley, dried
1 bay leaf
5 cloves garlic, copped
1 tsp black pepper, ground
1 cup wild rice or barley, cooked
Vegetable stock or water

Rinse beans and then soak overnight in water.

Drain beans and place in crockpot. Add vegetable juice, wine, soy sauce, and apple or pineapple juice. Cover with vegetable stock or water; the amount added depends on whether you prefer a soup (more liquid) or a stew (less).

Cook on high for 2 hours. Add vegetables, herbs, and spices, and cook for 5-6 hours on low until carrots and parsnips are tender. When tender, add rice and cook for one additional hour on low.

* For beans use 3 or 4 kinds, such as black, red kidney, pinto, baby lima, lentil, and green and/or yellow split peas. The more the merrier.

Thai Tomato Soup
Creamy, tangy, and simple

    1 tablespoon grated ginger
    2-3 cups chopped bok choy
    1/4 cup chopped fresh basil leaves
    2 cups stock or water
    48 oz. tomato juice
    3 tablespoons soy sauce
    1 cup bean sprouts
    1 cup lite coconut milk
    2 tablespoons lime juice
    (I add a little cayenne pepper too)

Cook the ginger, bok choy, and basil in the stock or water
in a medium stockpot for 10 minutes. Add the tomato juice,
soy sauce, and bean sprouts and cook another 10 minutes.
Add the coconut milk and lime juice and serve.
Makes 6-8 servings.

Vegetarian Green Chile

    1 large onion, chopped
    3-4 garlic cloves, crushed
    1 tablespoons olive oil
    6 cups vegetable stock
    12 roasted, peeled, chopped green chiles (adjust
        according to hotness of the chile)
    2 tablespoons flour or cornstarch
    Sea salt & pepper to taste

Saute onion and garlic in olive oil. Add chiles, then stock.
Add salt and pepper. Dissolve flour or cornstarch in a cup
of hot water and add to chile mixture. Simmer 45 minutes.

"Optional" ingredients:
    1 cup diced potato or white beans
    1 tomato, chopped
    1/2 cup cilantro, chopped

Ladle over eggs any style, add a flour tortilla, some fresh
shredded lettuce and a sprinkle of cheese.

Chickpea and Spinach Soup with Almonds and Garlic

Garbanzo beans (chick peas) are high in fiber, high quality protein, manganese, folate, copper and iron. Both garbanzo beans (due it's fiber) and garlic are great to lower cholesterol and maintain healthy blood sugar levels.... and the garbanzo beans and the onions are great for your bones!!!

Folate helps lower levels of homocysteine, an amino acid that is an intermediate product in an important metabolic process called the methylation cycle. Elevated blood levels of homocysteine are an independent risk factor for heart attack, stroke, or peripheral vascular disease, and are found in between 20-40% of patients with heart disease. It has been estimated that consumption of 100% of the daily value (DV) of folate would, by itself, reduce the number of heart attacks suffered by Americans each year by 10%. Just one cup of cooked garbanzo beans provides 70.5% of the DV for folate.

>   2 cups garbanzo beans, rinsed and soaked over night in cold water and refrigerated (or 3 cups canned, drained and rinsed)
>   2 tablespoons olive oil
>   2 onions, coarsely chopped, about 2 1/2 cups
>   7-8 cloves garlic, finely minced
>   1 potato, sliced, about 1 cup
>   5 cups chicken stock or more if needed
>   1 teaspoon sea salt
>   1/4 teaspoon freshly ground black pepper
>   4 tablespoons organic butter or olive oil
>   6 cups spinach, cut into thin strips and well washed
>   6 tablespoons sliced, toasted almonds, chopped
>   4 teaspoons finely minced garlic

1. Drain the soaked garbanzos, rinse well and put into a medium saucepan. Cover with fresh cold water. Bring to a boil and reduce heat. Simmer, covered, for about an hour

or until tender. Drain the cooked garbanzos and set aside.

2. Heat 1 tablespoons. olive oil in a large saucepan over moderate heat. Add the chopped onions and cook for about 10-15 minutes or until translucent. Add the garlic and stir for a minute or two. Then add the sliced potato, half the garbanzos, and the chicken stock and bring up to a boil. Simmer and cook until the potato and beans are falling apart, about 20 minutes.

3. Puree the soup in a blender. Season with salt and pepper. Just before serving, bring the soup up to a simmer. If it is too thick, thin it with more stock or water. In a very large saute pan, heat 2 teaspoon of oil and wilt the spinach. Add the pureed soup. Stir in the remaining whole cooked garbanzos.

4. In a small saute pan, over a medium heat, warm 1 teaspoon of oil. Saute the almonds with the teaspoon of finely minced garlic. Cook a few minutes and add these to the soup. Adjust seasoning. Serve at once.
Serves 6-8

A KEY TO STABLE BLOOD SUGAR LEVELS...

Combining protein and carbohydrates every time you eat.

Excellent food choices containing both protein and complex carbs:

Nuts, Beans, Lentils, Peas, Yogurt (plain), and Whole Grains such as Barley!

Texas Red Chili

1 onion, chopped
  1 cup chopped peppers (habanero, serrano, jalapeno, etc.
  2 cloves garlic chopped
  2 cans "mexican" style tomato sauce (containing chili's and jalapenos)
  1 bottle of beer (optional)
  2 tablespoons chili powder (or taco seasoning)
  3 tablespoons ground cumin
  1 tablespoon sea salt
  2 tablespoons black pepper
  2 pounds meat (hamburger or stew meat)
  2 tablespoons corn grits
  1 tablespoon oregano (preferably Mexican oregano crushed -- rubbed in between your palms)
  4-5 teaspoons cayenne pepper
  2 cups water
  3 cans organic beans (pinto, black, kidney, etc) drained and rinsed

1. Brown meat (but don't cook all the way because it will cook in the pot.)

2. Put all the ingredients in a crockpot, stir well. The longer everything cooks, the more the flavors mingle. It's best to set it on low for 8 hours or longer.

Serve with grated cheese, sour cream and flour tortillas.

1. Brown meat (but don't cook all the way because it will cook in the pot.)

2. Put all the ingredients in a crockpot, stir well. The longer everything cooks, the more the flavors mingle. It's best to set it on low for 8 hours or longer.

Serve with grated cheese, sour cream and flour tortillas.

Barbecue Pinto Beans

16 oz package dried pinto beans, rinsed and sorted
4 cups hot water
2 medium onions, chopped
1 tablespoons chili powder
3/4 cup hickory-flavored barbecue sauce (look for
     brands which do not add sugar or corn syrup)
1/2 cup natural ketchup (look for brands which do
     not add sugar or corn syrup)
1 1/2 tablespoons mustard
Tabasco sauce - as much as you like!

In your crock pot, mix together the beans, hot water, onions, and chili powder. Cover and cook on the low heat setting about 7 hours, or until the beans are tender but not falling apart.

Drain off all the cooking liquid. Stir in the barbecue sauce, ketchup, mustard, and Tabasco sauce. Cook, uncovered, 10 to 15 minutes longer, until heated through.

A KEY TO HEALTH...

Eat What God Told Us to Eat

I have given you every plant with seeds on the face of the earth and every tree that has fruit with seeds. This will be your meat (food). Genesis 1:29

Pink Lentil Curry

Pink Lentil Curry features magnesium-rich lentils. Several nutritional elements in lentils and this recipe may be helpful for people with diabetes.

Lentils are a wonderful source of protein, calcium, magnesium, and iron. They are a staple ingredient in Indian cooking, and combine well with many different seasonings. You may be most familiar with brown or green lentils, but did you know lentils can also be black, yellow and pink? Look for these more exotic varieties in Indian and specialty food stores. Note: All curry powders are not the same, ranging from mild to very hot. In making this dish, start with a small amount and taste it to be sure your dish meets your desire. This dish is filled with exotic flavor and can be served as an entrée with rice or as a side dish alone.

    1 pound pink lentils
    1 tablespoon olive oil
    1/2 cup carrots, chopped
    1/2 cup celery, chopped
    1 cup onion, chopped
    2 cups cabbage, chopped
    Curry powder, to taste - I use lots!
    4 cloves garlic, mashed
    1 tablespoon chopped ginger root
    1 tablespoon (or more) soy sauce or Bragg's Liquid
        Aminos
    4 cups hot cooked wild rice

1. Place lentils in pot with enough cold water to cover well. Bring to a boil, lower heat, and cook, partially covered, until lentils become a thick mush (about one hour).

2. Meanwhile, heat olive oil in skillet, add vegetables and a little water, stir and cover. Cook, stirring occasionally, until vegetables are barely tender.

3. Add curry powder, garlic and ginger. Stir, then replace cover and simmer until vegetables are tender.

4. Add vegetables and soy sauce to lentil mixture. Toss together, correct seasonings, and simmer for 10 minutes to blend flavors.

5. Serve with wild rice.
Serves 6

Rosemary Red Potatoes

Red potatoes, 6 cups, chopped into bite size pieces
4-5 cloves garlic, chopped
Olive oil, about 1/3 cup
Rosemary, preferably fresh! Lots!
Cayenne pepper, to taste
Sea salt, to taste
dijon mustard, 1 tablespoon (optional)

Mix ingredients in glass bowl. Add potatoes and mix together to coat. Place on cookie sheet and bake in hot oven - about 400 degrees for about 30-40 minutes. About half way through, turn potatoes to brown on all sides.

Parmesan Red Potatoes

Red potatoes, 6 cups, chopped into bite size pieces
1-2 cloves garlic, chopped
Olive oil, about 1/3 cup
Sea salt, to taste
1/2 cup parmesan cheese, grated

Mix ingredients in glass bowl. Add potatoes and mix together to coat. Place on baking sheet and bake in hot oven - about 400 degrees for about 40 minutes. About half way through, turn potatoes to brown on all sides.

Dill Fingerling Potatoes

1 pound fingerling potatoes, wash, but not peeled. Cut large ones in half.
2 tablespoons butter or olive oil
1 teaspoon sea salt
Freshly ground black pepper
2-3 tablespoons chopped fresh dill

1. Melt butter in large heavy bottom pan on stove on low.

2. Add potatoes salt and pepper and toss well.

3. Cover and cook for 20 - 30 minutes until potatoes are done.

4. Occasionally, shake the pot without removing lid to prevent burning.

5. Turn off heat and let potatoes sit for another 5 minutes.

5. Add dill, toss together and serve hot.

Roasted Sweet Potatoes with Cumin and Cilantro

2 orange-fleshed sweet potatoes, about 1 lb.
1 tablespoon olive oil
1 teaspoon ground cumin
Sea salt and freshly ground pepper
2 tablespoon finely chopped fresh cilantro

Preheat the oven to 400 degrees F. Cut the potatoes lengthwise into slices 1/2 inch thick. Stack half of the slices and cut lengthwise into strips 1/2 inch wide. Repeat with the remaining slices. Rinse the strips with cold water and spread on a clean kitchen towel; blot dry with a second kitchen towel. Place the potatoes in a bowl. Drizzle with the oil, sprinkle with the cumin, and toss to coat evenly.

Arrange the potatoes in a single layer on the hot baking sheet. Roast the potatoes, turning every 10 minutes, until evenly browned and tender when pierced with a knife, 30 to 35 minutes. Transfer the potatoes to a serving dish and sprinkle with 1/2 teaspoon salt, a grind of pepper, and the cilantro. Toss gently to coat. Serve at once.

Crockpot Sweet Potatoes

2 pounds sweet potatoes, grated or cut into small
    pieces
1/4 cup honey
1/4 cup butter, melted
1/4 cup flaked coconut
1/4 cup broken pecans -- toasted (optional)
1 teaspoon cinnamon

In a crock pot, combine potatoes, honey, butter, coconut, pecans and cinnamon. Cover and cook on low for 6 to 8 hours or on high for 3 to 4 hours.

Candied Yams

2 pounds sweet potatoes or yams
1/4 cup honey
1/8 cup real maple syrup
1/8 cup butter, melted (about 1/4 stick)
2 teaspoons cinnamon
1/2 teaspoon cloves

1. Boil yams or sweet potatoes in water till they are just soft, but not overdone. Remove and set aside to cool.

2. When cool, remove peeling and slice.

3. Place slices in a baking dish. Top with remaining ingredients.

4. Bake at 350 for 30 to 40 minutes. (or make in crockpot!)

Serve with turkey or other protein to balance the glycemic index!

Corn Bread

1/2 cup butter, melted
2 cups sour milk or buttermilk
1 1/2 cups yellow cornmeal
1/2 cup corn grits or course grain cornmeal
1 cup frozen corn kernels, thawed
1/3 cup honey (add some stevia if you like it sweeter)
1/2 teaspoon baking powder
1/4 teaspoon sea salt

In a small bowl, stir together butter, cornmeal, baking powder, and salt. Stir into corn mixture. Spread in a greased, 8-inch square baking pan. Cover lightly with foil. Bake at 350° for 50 minutes or until set. Let stand 15 minutes before cutting. Serves 8

Stuffed Green Peppers

1/2 of a 10 oz. package (5 oz) frozen corn kernels
1 can (15 oz) black beans drained and rinsed
1 can (14.5 oz) diced tomatoes (I use fire roasted)
1/4 cup salsa
1/4 cup chopped onions
1 1/2 cups cooked wild rice
1 teaspoon Bragg's Amino's or Worcestershire sauce
1/4 teaspoon sea salt
1/2 teaspoon red pepper
2 cups shredded cheddar cheese, divided
6 green peppers, tops removed & seeded

Combine all ingredients, except 1/4 cup cheese and green
peppers. Stuff peppers. Arrange peppers in crockpot.
Cover, cook on low 6-8 hours (high 3-4 hours). Sprinkle
with 1/4 cup cheese during the last 30 minutes. Makes 6
servings. Can also make in oven at 325 for about 40 minutes.

Spanish Rice

1 medium green bell pepper, diced
1 small onion, chopped
1 large clove garlic, chopped
2 14.5 oz. cans stewed tomatoes, undrained, Mexican
    style if desired
1 cup brown rice, uncooked
1 cup water
1/2 cup salsa, hot or mild
Tabasco® or Chalula® sauce as desired
Sea salt

Optional: Add 1/2 pound browned ground grass-fed beef,
and you have a meal!

This can be made in the crockpot or stove top.
Simply combine ingredients and turn on high or low for
crockpot.

For stovetop, place tomatoes, onions, garlic, rice and water
in pan and heat to boiling, reduce heat. Simmer on low for
about 1/2 hour.

Then add seasonings, pepper and salsa and cook until rice
and peppers are done.

Serves 4

Excellent side for Mexican dishes!

Green Bean Casserole
...the healthy way

I was always a big fan of Green Bean Casserole, but refused to use the canned soup it called for... this is what I came up with.

1/2 cup chopped onion
1 cup chopped celery
Saute in olive oil on medium low heat
Add 1 heaping tablespoon whole wheat flour and stir in
1 cup sour cream (I use low fat.)
Add a pinch of celery salt
Splash of Bragg's Amino's or light soy sauce.

Add two 14 ounce cans of french cut green beans (or can also use frozen) to the sour cream vegetable mixture, stir well and pour into a medium-sized buttered casserole dish.

Bake at 325 for 1 hour. Covered.

While this is in the oven, go back to your saute pan, and saute 3 or 4 (depending how large they are) thinly sliced leeks until carmelized. Save this for the topping.

For last 15 minutes uncover your green beans casserole and distribute the carmelized leeks evenly over the top.

This recipe also worked great if you want to add 2 cups of cooked wild rice (brown rice or barley would probably work fine as well). You may want to add a bit of extra sour cream to keep it moist. Bake in a large casserole dish, like a 9 x 13 glass. This makes a very filling meal!

WILD RICE DISHES

Whole grains, such as brown rice, quinoa and oats, are a great energy source. Grains supply complex carbohydrates, protein, vitamins, minerals and fiber. Wild rice is a delicious grain that isn't really rice at all. It's actually a long-grain marsh grass that grows wild in the Great Lakes area, parts of northern Minnesota and is cultivated commercially in California and the Midwest. When you use wild rice, be sure to rinse it thoroughly first. Set it in a bowl, cover it with water and let the debris float to the surface so you can pour it off. Don't cook it too long or you'll get starchy, wimpy grains that have lost much of their flavor.

Wild Rice and Mushrooms

> 1 cup porcini or shiitake mushrooms
> 2 1/2 cups water, approximately
> 1 cup wild rice
> 1/2 cup freshly squeezed orange juice
> 1/8 cup balsamic vinegar or red wine
> 1/2 cup sliced carrots
> 2 tablespoons chopped fresh parsley
> Cajun seasoning, salt or natural soy sauce to taste
> Optional: 1/2 cup finely chopped nuts

1. Wash the wild rice in cold water and place in pot with cold water.

2. Add the orange juice, wine and carrots. Bring to a boil, reduce heat, cover and simmer for 30 minutes.

3. Add mushrooms (presoak in water if they are dried) and continue cooking until rice is tender and all the liquid is absorbed.

4. Add the chopped parsley and salt or soy sauce to taste. Optional: Stir in finely chopped nuts (black walnuts, pecans or filberts).

Wild Rice Soup

2 cups cooked wild rice
Extra-virgin olive oil and butter to saute'
1 large onion chopped
2 cups celery, chopped
8-10 cloves garlic, chopped
2-3 raw chicken breasts, cut into bite size pieces
    (optional)
1/8 cup rice vinegar
1/2 cup dry white wine (optional)
About 30 ounces organic chicken broth
2 cups carrots, chopped
2 cups mushrooms, chopped
Other chopped optional vegetables - red bell pepper,
    cauliflower, etc.
Cayenne pepper
1-2 cups organic 1/2 and 1/2 (or raw whole milk)
Cornstarch or arrowroot to thicken
Lemon juice or sea salt as desired
Bragg's Liquid Amino's to taste

1. Saute' onion and garlic and celery in olive oil and butter for several minutes. If adding, chicken, add it now to brown it slightly.

2. Add the rice vinegar and cook several minutes longer then add the white wine and let that cook for several more minutes.

3. Add broth, carrots, mushrooms, cayenne pepper and other optional vegetables and cook/simmer until carrots and other vegetables are soft - about 30 minutes.

4. Add cooked wild rice, can add more water if soup is too thick. Let simmer for about 5-10 minutes

5. Add 1/2 and 1/2 or milk and slowly warm, stirring frequently so does not scorch. If it tastes flat, add Bragg's. lemon juice or sea salt as desired.

6. Serve and enjoy!

Broccoli Wild Rice

This is an easy main dishes to make. It's full of flavor and also has the cancer-fighting protection of broccoli.

> 1 cup wild rice, uncooked, rinsed
> Large bunch of broccoli
> 1 tablespoon extra-virgin olive oil
> Several cloves of garlic, chopped or mashed
> Chopped fresh mushrooms
> 1/2 cup water
> Salt or Cajun seasoning to taste
> Red pepper flakes
> Grated parmesan cheese (optional)

1. Cook the rice in rapidly boiling water or stock until done.

2. Trim the ends of the broccoli stems and cut off the flowers. Peel the outer fibrous layer off the main stalks and cut the stalks into bite-sized pieces.

3. Separate the flower of the broccoli into bite-sized pieces.

4. Place the broccoli in a colander and rinse under cold running water. Put it in a saucepan with the olive oil, garlic, water and salt. Bring to a boil, cover tightly, and let steam until the broccoli is bright green and very crunchy-tender - no more than 5 minutes. Remove the lid and boil off most of the remaining liquid.

5. Toss the broccoli with cooked rice.

6. Top with red pepper flakes and Parmesan cheese, if desired.

I often saute chopped mushrooms with the garlic and add these separately also.

Wild Rice with Peas and Garlic

2 cups cooked wild rice
8 oz. frozen peas (organic if possible)
Extra-virgin olive oil
6 cloves of garlic, chopped or mashed
8 oz. chopped fresh mushrooms
Bragg's Liquid Aminos to taste
Cajun seasoning or red pepper flakes to taste

1. Saute garlic and chopped mushrooms in olive oil for several minutes. Add Bragg's, cayenne pepper

2. Reduce heat and add peas long enough for them to unthaw and warm up.

5. Mix peas, mushrooms and garlic with cooked rice and serve.

KEYS TO HEALTHY COOKING...

Avoid frying and fried foods.

The high heat creates trans fatty acids which are carcinogenic (cause cancer) and known to increase risk of type 2 diabetes, heart disease, obesity and many other health problems.

Use only extra virgin olive oil and butter for cooking.

Make a spread by whipping 1/2 of each in your blender or processor. Keep it in the fridge and use it for everything! Use it to saute' (on medium heat), grill, on rice, vegetables, bread, etc.

Wild Rice Pancakes

(I created this recipe while working for the Anishinaabe Center, White Earth, MN. It was a huge hit!)

Separate yolks (3) from whites, beat whites until peaks from and set aside.

Mix well:
3 egg yolks
1/2 to 3/4 cup ricotta cheese
1 cup buttermilk (or milk)
1 cup cooked wild rice
few drops of stevia
2 tablespoons of real maple syrup

Mix together well:
1 cup wild rice flour, finely milled
1/2 cup whole wheat flour, finely milled
1 teas. baking powder
1 teas baking soda
Sea salt

Add flour mixture (not all at once) to batter according to desired thickness of batter - mine was pretty thick so I spread them out on the grill a little after pouring. You can add milk or water to thin them down a little if desired.

Gently fold in whites and 1 cup blueberries (frozen is OK)

Pour onto hot griddle. Flip when they are bubbling. Cook a few more minutes on second side.

Serve with real maple syrup.

I often serve soup at lunchtime or leftovers, but when you are in the mood for something a little different, here are a few quick and easy meals:

Turkey Wrap
(Great use for leftover turkey from Eric!)

  1 cup cooked turkey, chopped
  2 large organic tortillas
  2 tablespoons green onion chopped
  2 tablespoons grated carrot or other vegetable (bell
        pepper, sprouts, etc.)
  2 tablespoons chopped cucumber
  1 cup romaine or spinach, chopped
  3 tablespoons mayonnaise (recipe on page 99)
  Sea salt to taste

Warm tortillas in oven. Divide ingredients into the two tortillas and fold them up to make your wrap.

Quesadilla *(Grilled or Baked)*
Quesadillas can be made so many ways defending on what you have available and how much rime you want to spend preparing them. Here is a basic recipe from which you can add extra ingredients as you wish: Grilled chicken, beef, onion, mushrooms, peppers, etc.

  2 organic whole grain tortillas
  1 1/2 cups cheddar and or monterey jack, shredded
  1/2 cup spiced black beans
  Jalapenos, chopped - as many as you like
  Olive oil

1. Brush olive oil onto tortilla and place this side down on hot grill or baking sheet.

2. Add other ingredients and grill or bake in hot oven (about 400 degrees). till browned and cheese is melted. Tortilla can be flat or folded over - your choice.

4. Serve with fresh salsa and sour cream.
Serves 1-2

Pita, Feta and Riata *(It's Greek!)*

2 organic pita bread, cut in 1/2
Olive oil
4 oz. feta cheese, chopped into bite size pieces
1 cup plain yogurt
1/2 cup cucumber grated
Cumin, dash of
Kalamata olives
Tomato slices

1. Make Riata sauce by mixing yogurt, cucumber and cumin together.

2. Brush pita bread with olive oil and quickly warm and slightly toast on oven on broil. (could also be done in toaster without olive oil) Watch so it doesn't burn. remove from oven.

3. Fill pita bread with feta, tomato and riata! Enjoy with a few kalamata olives!
Serves 1-2

Roast Beef or Venison w/ Vegetables

3 pounds venison, beef roast oe bison
Olive oil
1 1/2 cups finely chopped onions
1 cup finely chopped carrots
1 cup finely chopped parsnips
1 cup finely chopped celery
10 cloves garlic, smashed
1 sprig fresh rosemary
4 cloves
3 bay leaves
1 teaspoon black peppercorns
5 cups dry red wine (1 bottle)
1 cup beef stock
8 ounces wild mushrooms or button mushrooms, cut up

1. Using olive oil, in large roasting kettle, brown roast on all sides, remove from kettle and set aside.

2. In same kettle, saute onion and celery till onions are translucent. Then add other vegetables (except mushrooms) and cook for several more minutes.

3. Set roast on top of vegetables. Add wine, beef stock and seasonings.

4. Bring to boil and reduce heat to simmer on stove top for 3 hours or in oven at 300 degrees for 3-4 hours. About 1 hour before done, add mushrooms.

5. Remove roast and place on serving plate. With a slotted spoon, remove vegetables and place them around the roast.

6. Place kettle back on stove (if it was in the oven) and turn heat up to reduce the broth. Spoon on top of roast and vegetables. Serve with wild rice cooked in beef stock.

Garlic Steak and Asparagus

1 12 oz. boneless beef top loin (strip) steak, cut
    about 3/4 inch thick
3 large cloves garlic, coarsely chopped
1/2 teaspoon cracked or coarsely ground black pepper
1/4 teaspoon sea salt
10 thin asparagus spears, course ends trimmed off
2 teaspoons garlic-flavored olive oil or olive oil
1/2 cup beef broth
1 tablespoon dry white wine
1/4 teaspoon dijon mustard

1. Rub the steak on both sides with a mixture of the garlic, pepper, and sea salt, pressing in the mixture with your fingers. Place the asparagus in a shallow dish and drizzle with the oil.

2. For sauce, in a medium skillet stir together the broth and wine. Cook over high heat for 4 to 5 minutes or until mixture is reduced to 1/4 cup. Whisk in mustard; keep warm.

3. Preheat an indoor electric grill on high setting. Place steak on the grill rack. If using a covered grill, close lid. Grill until steak is desired doneness. (For a covered grill, 3 to 4 minutes for medium rare or 5 to 7 minutes for medium. For an uncovered grill, 6 to 8 minutes for medium rare or 8 to 10 minutes for medium, turning steak once.)

4. Add asparagus to covered grill for the last 4 minutes or for uncovered grill the last 6 minutes of grilling. Cook asparagus until crisp-tender. (Thicker stalks may take longer)

5. Spoon sauce on serving plate. Cut steak in half crosswise. Place steak halves on top of sauce, with asparagus criss-crossed on top.

Serve with large green salad, garlic coleslaw or wild rice.
Serves 2

Beef (Bison or Venison) Mushroom Burgundy

2 to 2-1/2 pounds, of beef, bison or venison, any cut
1 tablespoon butter, plus 1 tablespoon olive oil
3 tablespoons flour
Sea salt to taste
Freshly ground black pepper to taste
Cayenne pepper to taste
6-8 cloves garlic, chopped
1 cup red or burgundy wine
2 cups beef consume' or broth
3 cups halved or quartered mushrooms
1 cup chopped green pepper (optional)
3/4 cup sour cream
3 cups cooked wild rice
1/4 cup sliced green onions

1. Preheat oven to 300 F. Cut meat into thin strips. Coat with flour, salt and pepper.

2. Brown strips on stovetop in butter and olive oil.

2. Place strips into casserole baking dish with a lid. Add garlic, wine, broth. Cover and cook in oven for about 2 hours.

3. Add mushrooms and green pepper is adding. Return for oven for another 30 minutes or until meat is very tender.

4. Turn off oven and remove casserole from oven. Stir in sour cream and adjust seasonings if necessary. Return to oven so it stays warm until you are ready to serve.

4. Serve with wild rice topped with green onions and large green salad.
Serves 4

Lemon Chicken
(Oven baked or grilled)

4-6 raw chicken breasts (bone in or boneless)
Marinate chicken in glass baking dish in refrigerator for 4-12 hours:

- 1/2 head of garlic - chopped (about 8-10 cloves)
- 3/4 cup lemon juice concentrate
- 3/4 cup olive oil
- 1/2 cup dry white wine
- Sea salt
- Fresh oregano, 1/2 cup (chopped)
- Red pepper
- Lemon slices

Bake at 350 degrees for about 25 minutes. The chicken can also be grilled. I think both ways are excellent, but if you bake it you can use the marinade on top of a green vegetable you are serving with the meal. It is excellent served with steamed brussels sprouts and wild rice or oven baked red potatoes.

This recipe can also be made with salmon!

A KEY TO HEALTHY EATING...

Moderation!

...But the fruit of the spirit is love, joy, peace, patience, kindness, goodness, faithfulness, gentleness and self-control...

Galatians 5:22-23

Chicken Parmesan

4 raw chicken breasts
1/2 head of garlic - chopped (about 8-10 cloves)
1 large can or 2 small cans of organic roasted
    tomatoes - (I like Muir Glen brand)
1 6 oz. jar of organic tomato paste
Italian seasoning - about 2 tablespoons
Cayenne pepper - I use lots
Parmesan cheese - about 1 cup
Asiago or romano cheese - about 1 cup

1. Place chicken on bottom of glass baking dish, add garlic, tomatoes and tomato sauce, add seasoning and stir a little to mix. Top with most of the cheese, reserving a little to add at last ten minutes of baking.

2. Bake at 325 degrees for about 50 minutes. (I prefer this method because I cover it for the first 40 minutes and then remove the cover the last 10 minutes so the cheese gets brown.)

Can also be made in a crockpot on high for 5 hours or on low for 8 hours.

Serve on wild rice.

HOT Wings *(Cause we like it HOT!!)*

12 raw chicken wings or drummies
1/3 cup honey
1/2 cup hot sauce (like Franks® or Chalula®)
1/2 BBQ sauce - (I like Trader Joe's as it has no high fructose corn syrup)
Tabasco®, to preference of heat level
Sea salt
Black pepper
Cayenne pepper to taste preference
Olive oil or coconut oil

1. Preheat oven to 450.

2. Put sauce ingredients in crockpot on low. Stir before adding chicken.

3. On large baking sheet, place wings or drummies, drizzle with a small amount of melted coconut oil or olive oil. sprinkle sea salt, fresh ground pepper and cayenne pepper if desired.

4. Bake for 10 minutes. remove sheet from oven, flip each piece over, sprinkle with sea salt, pepper and cayenne again and return to over for 10 more minutes.

5. Remove each piece and place in crockpot for 2-3 hours on low. Make sure each piece is covered with sauce. Stir occasionally.

Eggplant Parmesan

1 large eggplant
Olive oil
1/2 head of garlic, chopped (about 8-10 cloves)
1 large can or 2 small cans of organic roasted
    tomatoes *(I like Muir Glen brand)*
1 6 oz. jar of organic tomato paste
Italian seasoning - about 2 tablespoons
Cayenne pepper - I use lots
Parmesan Cheese - about 2 cups
Asiago or romano cheese - about 1 cup

1. Peel and slice eggplant. Soak eggplant submerged in salt water for about 4 hours. Remove from water and dry with paper towel.

2. Brush eggplant with olive oil and sprinkle with cayenne pepper and grill on both sides till soft. Place eggplant on bottom of glass baking dish, add garlic, tomatoes and tomato paste, add seasoning and stir a little to mix. Top with most of the cheese, reserving a little to add at last ten minutes of baking.

3. Bake at 325 degrees about 50 minutes. (I prefer this method because I cover it for the first 40 minutes and then remove the cover the last 10 minutes to brown.)

Can also be made in a crockpot on high for 5 hours or on low for 8 hours.

Serve on wild rice.

Vegetable Lasagna

9 lasagna strips - or raw cabbage leaves
6 cups mixed fresh vegetables, chopped (cauliflower,
    shredded carrots, bell pepper, etc.)
1 18 oz. jar (or homemade) meatless tomato sauce (I
    like mushrooms in mine)
cayenne pepper to taste - I like lots!
12 oz. low-fat, ricotta cheese
1/2 cup parmesan cheese
12 oz. mozzarella cheese, shredded
2 eggs
8 cloves garlic, chopped
Oregano
2-3 cups chopped fresh spinach (or 1 1/2 cups frozen)

1. Boil lasagna strips to al dente'. Drain and set aside to cool.

2. Combine cheeses, eggs, chopped spinach, garlic and oregano in large bowl.

3. In 9 x 13-inch glass baking dish, spread small amount of sauce. Put 3 strips of lasagna noodles or raw cabbage leaves on top. On top , spread 1/3 of the cheese mixture and pour 1/2 of the vegetables on top. Pour more sauce on top of the vegetables. Repeat lasagna, cheese, vegetables and sauce. End with lasagna. Pour rest of sauce and cheese on top. Top with extra Parmesan if desired.

4. Bake at 350 degrees for about 1 1/2 hours or until top browns.

Can be made ahead, covered with foil and left in warm oven for several hours before serving.

Serves 6.

Black Bean & Cheese Enchiladas

6 large organic tortillas
2 cups shredded natural white cheddar cheese
2 cans of organic black beans, drained (or about 3
    cups pre-cooked black beans)
2 cloves of garlic, chopped
2 tsp ground cumin
1 1/2 tablespoons red chili powder
Cayenne pepper to taste
Red enchilada sauce:
2 tablespoons butter
3 tablespoons flour
1/4 cup pure ground red chili
3 cups organic beef stock (2 14 oz. cans)
3/4 teaspoons sea salt
1 clove garlic, crushed
Pinch of Mexican oregano
Pinch of cumin
cayenne pepper, as desired

Melt butter over low heat in a saucepan. Add flour and stir until
well blended and slightly golden. Remove pan from heat. Stir in
broth, blending well. Add seasonings, cook, stirring for at least
10 minutes. Then simmer for at least 5 minutes.

To make enchiladas:
Dip tortillas in sauce. Add beans and cheese, roll and place
in 8 x 10 baking dish. Pour remaining sauce over the top.
Top with remaining cheese.
Bake at 350 for about 20 minutes.

Serve with:
    Fresh salsa (recipe on page 89.)
    Green onion, chopped
    1/2 cup shredded natural white cheddar cheese
    1-2 cups shredded romaine lettuce
    1 large avocado, cubed
    1 tomato, chopped
    Sour cream

Chicken in Mushroom Sauce

4 large or 8 small chicken thighs (2 to 2-1/2 pounds),
    trimmed of excess fat
2 teaspoons rotisserie or herb chicken seasoning
1 tablespoon butter
3 cups (8 ounces) halved or quartered mushrooms
1 medium onion, coarsely chopped
1/2 cup dry white wine
1/2 cup sliced green onions
Cayenne pepper to taste
Sea salt to taste
3/4 cup sour cream
Cooked wild rice or mashed potatoes

1. Sprinkle meaty side of chicken with seasoning. In large skillet over medium-high heat, melt butter. Add chicken, seasoned-side down; cook 3 minutes. Reduce heat to medium-low; turn chicken over.

2. Add mushrooms, onion and wine. Cover; simmer 15 to 18 minutes or until chicken is no longer pink inside.

3. Add sour cream and heat until it is warm to serve, but not boiling.

4. Serve with mashed potatoes or wild rice and green vegetable or large green salad.

Serves 4

Broccoli Chicken

Wild rice cooked in chicken broth (about 4 cups)
Organic chicken broth
2 tablespoons butter
1 teaspoon dried basil
1 teaspoon dried thyme
4 good sized boneless, skinless chicken breast halves
2 cups broccoli
1 tomato, chopped
Sea salt to taste
1 cup (4 ounces) shredded mozzarella or cheddar
    cheese

1. In large skillet over medium heat, brown chicken breasts
in   butter. Cook about 10-12 minutes till almost done.
Remove from skillet and set aside

2. Place cooked rice in skillet and add snout 1/2 to 1 cup
chicken broth, basil and thyme. Bring to a boil.

3. Place chicken over rice. Add broccoli and tomato.
Cover; simmer 10 minutes or until rice is tender and chick-
en is no longer pink inside. Sprinkle with cheese. Cover; let
stand 3 minutes or until cheese is melted.

Serves 4

Orange Glazed Turkey Breast with Cinnamon

Great any time of the year!

1 (about 5 pounds) turkey breast, with skin, deboned
Freshly grated orange peel from 1 large orange (about
    1 tablespoon)
1/2 cup orange juice
1 teaspoon ground cinnamon
Ground cloves, pinch

1. Preheat the oven to 350 degrees. Butter roasting pan or large casserole dish. Set aside.

2. In a small saucepan, combine the orange peel, orange juice, cinnamon and cloves. Bring to a boil; reduce the heat and simmer about 5 minutes. Remove the glaze from the heat and set aside.

3. Rinse the turkey breast in cool water and pat dry. Lay it in the roasting pan, breast-side-up. Pour all of the glaze over the turkey breast. Place in the preheated oven and roast, uncovered, for 2 to 2-1/2 hours, until a meat thermometer registers 170 to 175 degrees internal temperature. Brush the turkey with the glaze and surrounding juices periodically. Remove from the oven and let stand for 10 minutes before serving.

To serve, slice the turkey and ladle a small amount of the glaze and mixed juices over the slices. Serve the leftover glaze on the side.

Serves 10.

Yellow Squash with Pasta

This beautiful and complete meal may be served cool or at room temperature.

3 tablespoons olive oil
1 cup fresh fennel stalks, finely chopped
1/2 cup red onion slivers
2 cloves garlic, minced

Zest from 1 lemon
1/4 cup fresh lemon juice (1 large lemon)
1/2 teaspoon sea salt
3 yellow crookneck squash (1 pound), ends trimmed,
         cut into bite size pieces

6 cups water
2 cups whole grain fusilli pasta

8 ounces feta cheese
2 tablespoons fresh ginger juice (about 3 inches
         ginger root, grated and squeezed) - optional
2 tablespoons Bragg's Amino's

1. Saute onion, garlic and fennel in olive oil.

2. Add next four ingredients and saute until squash is tender, but do not overcook. When done, transfer to a serving bowl.

3. Bring 6 cups water to boil; add pasta, cook until barely al dente, and drain.

4. Stir in Braggs' to taste and add feta to squash mixture and toss all together and serve.

NOTE: I also like to add a bit of cayenne pepper... (-:

Jalapeno Mac and Cheese

This is surely an adult recipe for a childhood favorite, although I have no idea why kids would not like it as it really is not hot with all that creamy cheese!

8 ounces dry whole grain pasta of your choice: spirals, elbow, egg noodles, etc.
Water to boil
2 tablespoons butter
1/2 white onion, chopped
1 cup jalapenos chopped, red and green
1 heaping tablespoon whole wheat flour
1 cup milk
2 tablespoons Tabasco
1/2 teaspoon sea salt
1/2 teaspoon cayenne pepper... or to taste
1 cup of jalapenos in a jar with juice
1 pound fontina cheese, grated
4 oz. of cream cheese, I use low fat
1/2 cup other white cheese - mozzarella, white cheddar, etc.

1. Prepare pasta as directed on package and cook until al dente. Drain when ready.

2. Saute onions in butter until softened, add jalapenos, when softened add flour and stir.

3. Add milk and stir until boiling (no higher than medium heat).

4. Place 1/2 of sauce, cream cheese and juice from canned jalapenos in processor and process until pureed.

5. Return to pan, add salt, Tabasco, cayenne, and cheeses a small amount at a time.

5. Combine with cooked pasta, toss. Add more milk if needed.

Chicken Fettuccine with Red Pepper Sauce

12 ounces dry fettuccine whole wheat pasta
(could also use spaghetti or even egg noodles)
3 or 4 small chicken breasts, boneless, cut into bite size
pieces
Extra virgin coconut oil or olive oil to sautee
1 red bell pepper, julienned
4 red jalapeno peppers, julienned
1 very small yellow onion, chopped fine
3 cloves garlic, minced
3/4 teaspoon cayenne pepper
1 tablespoon taco seasoning (no MSG)
1 cup reduced fat (or fat free) sour cream
1/2 cup organic chicken broth
1/2 cup grated Parmesan cheese
Sea salt and pepper to taste

1. Bring a large pot of lightly salted water to a boil. Add pasta and cook for 8 to 10 minutes or until al dente; drain and keep warm.

2. Meanwhile, in a large skillet saute onion until translucent, add garlic and cook a few minutes longer.

3. Add chicken pieces, sea salt, cayenne pepper, taco seasoning and cook until done. Remove chicken from pan and keep warm in oven.

4. Add red jalapeno and bell peppers to pan and saute over medium heat for 3 to 5 minutes.

5. Stir in sour cream and broth; simmer for 2 minutes and add in chicken and cooked pasta. Toss altogether. Season as needed. Remove from heat.

6. Serve on warm plates or bowls and top with cheese.

Bison Meat Loaf

Bison is considered "healthier" than beef, due to it's very low fat content. I actually prefer the taste over beef, as it seems a little sweeter. Cooking bison is similar to cooking with beef except that because the fat content is so low you do need to make sure to add some olive oil to the meat or it seems a little dry.

1 and 1/2 to 2 pounds raw ground bison
2 eggs
1-2 gloves garlic minced
1 teaspoon sage
1/4 cup freshly ground flax seeds
2 tablespoons rolled oats
2 tablespoons olive oil
1 teaspoon sea salt
Fresh ground black pepper
Cayenne to taste
Tablespoon of BBQ sauce. (I like Traders Joes -
  natural with no high fructose corn syrup (HFCS)

Sauce: 1/2 cup BBQ sauce
       1/2 cup natural ketsup (organic with no sugar or
       HFCS.

1. Mix together, place and form loaf in well oiled (olive oil) glass baking dish. I use a 6 x10 size.

2. Mix sauce together and cover meat loaf. Cover with tin foil and bake at 350 degrees for about 1 hour.

Bison Meat Balls

1 and 1/2 pounds raw ground bison
2 or 3 eggs
2-4 gloves garlic, minced
1 and 1/2 teaspoons Italian seasoning
1/4 cup freshly ground flax seeds
2 tablespoons olive oil
1 teaspoon sea salt
Fresh ground black pepper
Cayenne pepper to taste
2/3 cup chopped fresh basil
High quality parmesan cheese, grated

1. Mix together, form balls (I like to use an ice cream scooper) and place on baking sheet lined with foil and olive oil. Make sure you have enough olive oil or they will stick. I like to use the foil for easy clean up.

2. Bake at 400 degrees for about 10 minutes. Remove from oven and carefully turn each one with a tong. Return to oven for another 10 minutes or so.

3. Serve with your favorite sauce and pasta or wild rice. You can also try steamed shredded cabbage as a healthy low calorie carb alternative!

Michael's Grilled Bison Patty Melt

1/2 to 3/4 pounds raw ground bison
Mix meat with olive oil, sea salt, fresh ground black pepper and cayenne pepper. Shape into 2 or 3 patties.
Grilled green bell pepper and onion
Rye bread, grilled
Pepperjack cheese

Shredded Bison or Chicken

I make this in the crockpot and use for tacos, enchiladas, burritos, to make pizza, etc.

Bison roast (3 to 4 pounds) **OR**
    Boneless chicken breasts (about 5)
1 medium sized onion, chopped
4-6 jalapeno peppers, red and/or green, chopped
1 glove garlic, chopped
1/2 cup brown lentils or presoaked black beans (for bison) **OR**
    1/2 cup red lentils (for chicken)
1/2 cup enchilada sauce or salsa
1/4 cup taco seasoning (no MSG)
Cayenne pepper to taste
Sea salt
Black pepper

Place all ingredients in crockpot and cook on high. Bison will take at least 5 hours depending on the size of the roast. Chicken will only take about 3 hours. Can also cook chicken on low for about 5 or 6 hours.

When meat is totally falling part it is ready to shred. Take two forks and shred or break apart with a spoon or two.

If too wet, remove cover and let cook for another hour or two. If too dry add more enchilada sauce or salsa.

If too spicy for your taste, add low fat sour cream.... This is especially tasty with the chicken so you may want to add it anyway!

Leftovers keep well and and can be reheated in the oven.

SALMON RECIPES
SALMON RECIPES

Salmon is by far my favorite "meat." A very important part of serving a great salmon dish to to **buy it fresh**. *If it smells fishy - don't buy it (yes, I do ask to smell it!). Ask the meat department when it came in or find out what days they get it in - and buy it that day!! I don't like it frozen if at all possible. To me it tastes fishy.*

Salmon is easy to cook and elegant to serve. I cook it often - at least every week. Here are a few of my favorite ways:

Roasted Salmon

Prep. time: 10 minutes (plus1 hour marinating).
Cooking time: about 10 minutes. Serves 4.

    4 6-8 oz salmon fillets, center-cut, skin on
    1 tablespoons. olive oil
    1 tablespoons. fresh lemon juice
    1 tablespoons. chopped fresh rosemary
    Salt and freshly ground pepper, to taste

Dry salmon with paper towel. Whisk together the oil, lemon juice, rosemary and pepper. Rub onto salmon, covering all sides, place on a plate, cover loosely and allow to marinate refrigerated for 1 hour.

Preheat oven to 425° F (220° C). If your non-stick skillet does not have an oven-proof handle double wrap it in aluminum foil.

Brush skillet with olive oil and preheat.

Remove salmon from fridge and lightly season with salt.

Place salmon flesh side down in very hot pan to sear for 1 minute. Immediately place hot pan with salmon into the hot oven and roast for 8 minutes.

Salmon should flake when pressed with a fork when done.

Seared Salmon w/ Orange Glaze

4 (6-8 oz each) salmon fillets, skinned if desired
1 tablespoons sesame oil, preferably untoasted
Glaze:
3 tsp low-sodium soy sauce (or Bragg's Amino's)
1/3 cup white wine
1/3 cup frozen orange juice concentrate
1 tablespoon cornstarch (optional)
1 tsp grated or minced orange zest
1/2 tsp peeled, grated or minced ginger root

1. Pat salmon dry. Preheat oven to 400 degrees F. Have ready a glass baking dish large enough to hold salmon in a single layer.

2. In a nonreactive small saucepan over medium-high heat, heat orange glaze ingredients; simmer, stirring frequently, about 15 minutes until sauce is thickened. Add orange slices and cook, stirring once or twice. Remove from heat.

3. In a large skillet over medium-high heat, heat oil. Add salmon and sear, turning once, 1 minute on each side. You should hear fish sizzle. Transfer salmon to baking dish and drizzle with orange glaze. Transfer to oven and roast 10 minutes until cooked through and flakes easily.

Transfer salmon to individual plates and serve immediately.
Yield: 4 servings

Serving suggestion: Serve the salmon on a dark green salad, sauteed spinach or with other steamed greens such as broccoli or Brussels sprouts. The orange sauce mixed together with these is excellent!

NOTE: If the skin is removed I have skipped the searing step and just baked the salmon. Just place salmon in a glass baking dish and pour orange glaze over the top. Bake for about 15 minutes uncovered. Then broil for a minute minutes for the final effect. Just watch it closely.

Dijon Salmon on Wild Rice

2-3 cups hot cooked wild rice
1/4 cup Kalamata olives, pitted and sliced in half
1 tablespoons olive oil
1/4 tsp sea salt
2 tablespoons fresh dill or parsley, chopped
1 cup carrots julienned
1 cup zucchini, julienned
1 cup asparagus tips
1 cup red bell pepper, julienned
Salmon fillets, four 6-ounce pieces
4 tablespoons dijon mustard (horseradish style is good)
4 large sheets of parchment paper or tin foil

1. Heat oven to 400 degrees.

2. Cook wild rice in boiling water or stock until done (about 45 minutes), toss with a bit of olive oil, olives, salt and chopped fresh dill or parsley.

3. Rinse salmon fillets and pat dry. Spread dijon mustard evenly over the top of each one.

4. Prepare the parchment or tin foil; Place about 1/2 cup of the rice in the center, top with a salmon fillet, and add the vegetables. Bring the sides of the paper or tin foil over the fish and fold the edges together starting at the top. Fold over several times to secure it.

5. Place the pouches in the middle of the hot oven and bake for 15 minutes. Serve immediately in the sealed pouches, opening them just before eating. Serves 4.

Grilled Salmon w/ Vegetables

1. Use whole salmon of any type. Leave the skin on as it lifts right off after cooking. Place the salmon on a piece of foil large enough to completely wrap it. I make mine in individual servings.

2. Fill the inside of the salmon "bowl" with a mixture of chopped: Onion, carrots, garlic, red and green peppers, zucchini or asparagus.
     2 or 3 slices of lemon
     1/4 cup white wine and 1/4 cup lemon juice
     2 tablespoons butter
     2 ounces rich cheese like havarti
     Salt and pepper to taste.

3. Seal the foil and cook on a grill or in an oven at 350 degrees. The cooking time depends on the size/amount of fish. (usually about 30 minutes) Open the foil and test the fish for flakiness. The vegetables usually absorb a lot of flavor from the fish.
Serve on wild rice!

This recipe also works well using halibut, walleye, orange roughly or other white fish.

Easy Grilled Salmon

This is my favorite way to prepare fresh salmon fillet of any type with skin on. I always look for wild if it's available.

Brush flesh side of fillet with olive oil and salt lightly.

Place skin side down onto hot grill for a few minutes and flip. Cook for a few minutes longer and then turn 1/4 turn to obtain "X" grill marks. I sometimes like to cover the fish when it is cooking to prevent any moisture loss. The fish is done when it flakes apart when pressed with a fork. The skin peels off easily.

(This also works well for steelhead trout and other firm fish)

Poached Salmon

Small salmon fillets, approximately 6 ounces, are poached by putting about a half inch of water in a small, 5-6 inch fry pan, covering it, heating the water to simmer, then putting in the fillet covered for four minutes. Add whatever seasoning you like to the salmon or to the water. The four minutes leaves the center uncooked and very juicy. Cook longer if desired.

Fillets may be served whole or cut it into inch and a half wide pieces and added to a dark green salad with tomato, ripe avocado, red onion, croutons, and any tasty dressing.

Citrus Salmon

  1 lb salmon fillet, cut into two
  Sea salt and pepper
  1 tablespoon cornstarch
  1 tablespoon water
  3 tablespoons frozen orange juice conc.
  1 tablespoon lemon juice
  1/8 cup honey
  Garnish (optional): 1 sliced orange/parsley

1. Sprinkle both sides of the salmon fillet with salt and pepper.

2. Mix the cornstarch and water in a small bowl to form a paste. Add the orange juice concentrate, lemon juice and brown sugar. Stir mixture well until all the ingredients are dissolved. Set aside.

3. Pour 1/2 of the sauce into the bottom of a glass dish. Place the salmon fillet in the dish on top of sauce. Pour remaining sauce over the salmon. Cover the dish with foil.

4. Bake at 375 for about 20 minutes till salmon is done.

5. Stir remaining sauce from baking dish and pour over the fillets and garnish if desired.

Serves 2.

Fusilli w/ Baked Tomatoes and Salmon

From "Totally Salmon" by Helene Siegel, Celestial Arts

1/8 cup olive oil
5 medium tomatoes, cored and cut in small wedges
1 1/2 lbs. skinless salmon fillet, cut into 1 inch cubes
1/2 cup thinly sliced fresh basil or sorrel
1 tablespoons. minced garlic
Sea salt and freshly ground pepper
1 lb. fusilli or corkscrew pasta

1. Preheat oven to 400 degrees F.

2. Lightly coat a medium ceramic or glass baking dish with some of the oil. Cover the bottom half with half of the tomatoes. Top with half of the salmon, the garlic, and basil or sorrel. Salt and pepper. Repeat the layers and seasoning. Drizzle lightly with rest of oil.

3. Bake uncovered for 20 to 25 minutes until tomatoes soften and juices run together, stirring once.

4. While baking, cook the pasta in a large pot of salted water, drain and transfer to a serving bowl. Top with roasted sauce and toss well.

Serves 4.

A KEY TO HEALTHY EATING...

Eat To Satisfy the Nutritional Needs of the Body, Not Just Feed the Flesh

So, whether you eat or drink, or whatever you do, do all to the glory of God. 1 Corinthians 10:31

Salmon-Broccoli Loaf w/ Dill & Capers *from Jean Anderson's Processor Cooking*

- 1 cup loosely packed parsley sprigs, washed and patted dry on paper towels
- 6 slices firm-textured white bread
- 2 cups 1/2 inch cubes of broccoli stems
- 1 medium yellow onion, cut into slim wedges
- 1 3/4 pounds cooked or canned boned salmon (remove all dark skin)
- 1/3 cup drained capers (use the small capers)
- 2/3 cup light cream (can use non-fat evaporated milk)
- 4 eggs
- 2 tablespoons. snipped fresh dill or 3/4 tsp dill weed
- Finely grated rind of 1/2 lemon
- 1/8 teaspoon freshly ground black pepper

1. In food processor fitted with metal chopping blade, mince parsley fine, using 5-6 on-offs of the motor; empty into a large mixing bowl. Crumb the bread 2 slices at a time, with two or three 5-6 on-offs; add to bowl. Dump all the broccoli stems into processor; mince very fine with about three 5-second bursts; add to bowl.

2. In the processor-mince the onion -- 3 or 4 bursts -- add to the bowl.

3. Flake the salmon in three batches -- 2 on-offs will be enough. Add to the mixing bowl along with all remaining ingredients. Mix thoroughly.

4. Pack mixture firmly into a well-buttered 9x5x3 inch loaf pan and bake in a slow oven (300 degrees F.) for about 1 hour and 40 minutes, or until loaf begins to pull from sides of pan and is firm to the touch.

5. Remove loaf from oven and **let it stand upright in its pan on a wire rack for 30 minutes**. Carefully loosen the loaf all around with a thin-bladed spatula, then invert gently onto a large serving platter.

Salmon Limone

One of my favorites adapted from Spasso's Family Italian Restaurant in Laguna Hills, CA

3/4 lb. skinless salmon fillet, poached/cut into two pieces
1/3 cup olive oil
1/2 cup lemon juice
2 tablespoons capers
Minced garlic to taste
Bite-sized pieces of carrot, cauliflower, and broccoli - lightly steamed
Cooked angle hair whole grain pasta

Mix olive oil and lemon juice and combine with vegetables and capers, toss lightly in pasta, divide onto plates and place salmon on top. Serves 2.

Herbed Poached Salmon
(Crockpot or oven)

Salmon fillets (2-4)
1 cup water
1 cup white wine
1 tsp sea salt
2 bay leaves
2 peppercorns
1 sprig fresh rosemary
1 slice red onion
Fresh oregano or thyme
Sprigs fresh parsley

Lightly grease the bottom of your crockpot or baking dish, then place the salmon cutlets (or filets) in the bottom. Put the remaining ingredients in a pan and heat until boiling. Pour over the salmon, put the lid on your crockpot or baking dish.
For crockpot, cook on low for about 3 hours.
For oven, cook at 375 for about 15-20 minutes

Serve hot, or cold with a salad.

Spicy Salmon and Eggplant

Recipe by: Judy Dinardo-Namak

3 fresh salmon steaks
1 eggplant
3 limes
2 lemons
1/8 cup olive oil
1 teaspoon Greek or Italian seasoning
1/8 teaspoon hot red pepper flakes
Fresh ground black pepper

1. Remove stem and end of eggplant and slice on a diagonal, cutting slices approximately 1/4-inch thick.

2. Place salmon steaks and eggplant slices in a large, flat plastic container.

3. Cut lemons and limes in half and remove juice. Pour juice into a separate bowl. Stir in olive oil, seasoning, pepper flakes and ground pepper. Pour over steaks and eggplant. Cover and marinate in refrigerator for 1 to 1-1/2 hours.

4. Turn steaks over and rearrange eggplant for even marinating, once during process.

5. Cook steaks on a hot grill on both sides until done.

6. Add eggplant slices to grill when fish is half cooked. Grill eggplant slices on both sides. Remove.

7. Serve fish and vegetables with rice. Serve hot.

Thai Salmon Parcels for 2

from Delia Smith's summer collection

> 2 4-5 ounce salmon fillets
> 4 sheets filo pastry
> 1 ounce butter
> Zest & juice of 1 lime
> 1 teaspoon grated ginger
> 1 clove garlic (pressed)
> 1 spring onion (finely chopped)
> 1 tablespoons fresh coriander (finely chopped)
> Salt & pepper

1. Mix together lime zest and juice, garlic, spring onion, ginger and coriander.

2. Melt butter. Lay out 1 sheet of filo, and brush with butter. Lay second sheet on top, brush with more butter. Lay a salmon fillet about 2-3 inches from short side of pastry, season to taste and put half of lime mixture on top.

3. Fold short end of pastry over salmon, then fold in the 2 long sides. Fold the salmon over twice more, and cut off the remaining pastry. Do the same with the other fillet.

4. Put the parcels on a well-greased baking sheet, and just before baking brush with the remaining butter. Cook at medium heat for 20-25 minutes, until brown and crispy.

Serves 2

OTHER TYPES OF FISH

Orange Teriyaki Tuna

4 fresh tuna steaks, about 6 ounces each

Marinate in shallow glass baking dish for 1-2 hours. Turn steaks over one or twice in that time. Keep covered in refrigerator.

To make marinade, mix together:
- 1/4 cup Bragg's Liquid Aminos or teriyaki sauce
- 1/4 cup fresh orange juice
- 3 strips orange zest
- 3 tablespoons honey
- 1 1/2 tablespoons sesame oil
- 3 cloves garlic, crushed with the side of a cleaver
- 3 slices (1/4" thick) fresh ginger, minced

- 1 tablespoon toasted sesame seeds for garnish
- 1/4 cup chopped scallion greens for garnish

1. Preheat the grill to high. Lift tuna steaks out of the marinade and place on grill.

2. Pour the remaining marinade into a small saucepan and boil to a thick, syrupy glaze.

3. Grill the fish until cooked to taste, about 4 to 6 minutes per side for medium. As each side is cooked, brush it with the glaze (the boiled marinade).

4. Sprinkle the tuna with chopped scallion greens and sesame seeds and serve at once.

177

Grilled Seared Tuna Steaks with Basil Butter

Basil Butter Recipe
3 cups fresh basil leaves
1 stick soft organic butter (1/2 cup)
1/2 teaspoon Sea salt
1 tablespoon lemon juice
1/4 cup olive oil
1 tablespoon capers (optional)
pinch of cayenne pepper (optional)
1 clove garlic (optional)

Place all ingredients in processor except olive oil, I like to slowly drizzle it in as the processor is running.

This can be used on fish, on veggies, or to make crusty cheese bread. It can be made and frozen when basil is ready to harvest and used all winter long!

Tuna steaks - 1 per person
Olive oil
Lemon Juice
Sea salt
Flat glass container to briefly marinate fish

Tuna steaks are briefly marinated in lemon juice and olive oil. Add sea salt on both sides and place on hot grill (450 degrees) for total of 3 minutes. (if you have an indoor grill, close and you do not have to flip it. If you have an outdoor grill, cook for about 90 seconds per side.) If you check it, it will still be pink (raw looking inside). It is ready to serve as it will continue cooking after removing from the grill.

Remove from grill, place and top with a tablespoon of basil butter.

Baked Parmesan-Crusted Cod with Spinach

2 fresh cod fillets (or 1 per person)
1 tablespoon Basil butter (recipe on previous page)
    (softened)
Grated Parmesan cheese about 2 tablespoons
Natural croutons crushed - about 2 tablespoons
    (I get mine from Trader Joe's)
16 ounces baby spinach
1/2 tablespoon lemon juice
Sea salt and freshly ground black pepper
Crushed red pepper
Olive oil

1. Preheat oven to 425 degrees.

2. In a small bowl mix 1 tablespoon Basil butter with 2 table-spoons crouton crumbs and parmesan cheese.

3. In glass baking dish, place a few drops olive oil and spread throughout bottom and partway up sides.

4. Place raw spinach evenly along bottom.
Top spinach with lemon juice.

5. On top of spinach lay cod fillets spaced evenly apart.

6. Sprinkle spinach and fish with sea salt and freshly ground black pepper

7. Spread a layer of basil butter /crouton crumbs/Parmesan cheese on top each piece of fish.

8. Bake in hot oven for about 10 minutes. For the last minute, you can place under broiler to help brown the topping or use a kitchen torch which I prefer to avoid scorching the spinach.

This recipe works well with any mild white fish - halibut, orange roughly, etc.

EZEKIEL BREAD

(Basic Recipe)
Mill the following into fine flour:
   2 1/2 cups Hard Red Wheat
   1 1/2 cups Spelt or Rye or Flax or (1/2 and 1/2)
   1/2 cup Barley
   1/4 cup Millet
   1/4 cup Lentils
   2 tablespoons Great Northern Beans
   2 tablespoons Red Kidney Beans
   2 tablespoons Pinto Beans

Measure into a large bowl:
   4 cups warm water
   1 cup honey or molasses *(can reduce & add stevia)*
   1/3 cup olive oil
   2 tablespoons yeast

Mix and set aside *(I place in the oven at 100 degrees)* for 5-10 minutes or until frothy.

Add to the yeast 2 tsp salt and all the flour

Mix with a strong wooden spoon until stretchy and elastic - about 7 minutes. (I actually use the mixer.)

This is a batter bread that will not form a smooth ball. Pour into 3 greased bread pans in even amounts.

Place pans in oven on lowest heat to rise (100-120 degrees). Allow to rise to within 1/2 inch of tops of pans or it may overflow, about 15-20 minutes.

Once risen, WITHOUT OPENING THE DOOR, turn the heat up to 350. If you open the door, the cool air may cause the bread to fall. Bake at 350, about 25-30 minutes until nicely browned on top - This is a cake-like bread and will not be like regular yeast breads. You may have to experiment with cooking times.

> *Take thou also unto thee wheat, barley, beans, lentils, millet and fitches (spelt), and put them in one vessel, and make thee bread thereof.* Ezekiel 4:9

The basic recipe can be used to make many varieties. I often add cinnamon and raisins, or to make garlic bread, add chopped garlic. After baking the bread, I slice it into pieces and spread a little garlic butter on each one. Place them on a baking sheet under broiler for a few minutes and you have awesome garlic toast!

Almond Ezekiel Bread

Start with the basic recipe and then add about 3/4 cup slivered almonds, 2 teaspoons almond extract, 1 teaspoon cinnamon and 1 teaspoon cardamom. After placing dough into bread pans I sprinkled a few more slivered almonds on top.

Orange-Coconut Ezekiel Bread

Start with the basic recipe and then add about 1/4 cup frozen orange juice concentrate, 1/2 cup coconut (I used unsweetened). If you want before serving, you could drizzle the top with a honey and orange juice concentrate glaze.

Focaccia (Italian-Herb Bread)
Pizza Crust or Bread Sticks

Start with the basic Ezekiel bread recipe. Add about 1/4 cup shredded Parmesan cheese, 1/8 cup italian seasonings, 2-4 cloves garlic, minced, and a little extra course sea salt on top.

Form into the desired shape (sprinkle some extra cheese on if you wish) and let raise in warm oven.

Thin Crust Pizza

Makes 2 good sized pizzas

1 and 1/2 cups warm water
3 and 1/2 cups flour
   I use a combination of wheat, barley and rye.
1/8 cup olive oil (save some to oil pans)
1 and 1/2 teaspoons sea salt
Yeast - 1 packet
1 teaspoon of honey
Corn meal

Toppings of your choice (see next page for ideas)

1. Dissolve yeast in warm water and honey in warm place.
2. Add flour, salt and yeast and stir, knead until dough forms,(I like to add a few tablespoons of corn meal to my dough - I like the flavor)
3. Preheat oven to 425 degrees
4. Divide dough into two
5. Cover your baking pans with olive oil and a sprinkle of corn meal.
6. Place dough in middle of pan and spread so it thinly covers the sheet.

If your pan is too large for dough to cover, just make it 2/3 or 3/4 full, to the thinness you want the dough to be.

7. Prebake in preheated oven for 10 minutes.

8. Remove and cover with desired toppings.

9. Return to 425 degree oven for another 10-15 minutes until cheese is bubbling and browning slightly.

If you let it set for about 5 minutes it serves better, but it may be too hard to wait this long!

My Favorite (Mushroom, Spinach w/ Blue Cheese):

Sauteed mushrooms, onions and garlic (seasoned with cayenne pepper and sea salt)
Fresh, thinly sliced red jalapeno
Fresh spinach leaves
White cheese and blue cheese, but not too much blue cheese as it is very strong.

Michael's Favorite (Meat Lovers!!!) *Of course*

Sauteed mushrooms, onions and garlic (cayenne pepper and sea salt)
Browned ground bison with Italian seasonings, sea salt, black pepper and cayenne.
Thinly sliced natural beef sausage (works like pepperoni)
Fresh green bell pepper, chopped or sliced
Fresh red onion slivers
White and yellow cheese

Mexican (or Taco Pizza)

Leftover taco meat with black beans
Fresh, thinly sliced jalapenos - red and green
Fresh green bell pepper, chopped or sliced
Fresh red onion slivers
Grape or cherry tomatoes, cut in half or quarters
White and/or yellow cheese

FLAX RECIPES

Flax is one of my favorite foods. It provides the three main components that most people are missing in their diet today.

1. **Minerals**
2. **Omega-3 fatty acids**
3. **Fiber - soluble and insoluble**

It also promotes a healthy alkaline pH in the body and has a very low glycemic index. This makes flax a valuable ingredient for diabetics or someone concerned about their blood sugar. Adding flax to a food which would otherwise have a high glycemic index (see index for food list) will LOWER the glycemic index of that food. Glycemic index refers to the impact eating a food has upon one's blood sugar.

Flax seed is an excellent whole food high in fiber. It is rich in very important nutritional components which are otherwise hard to find: lignins, a cancer-fighting fiber and also the Omega-3 essential fatty acids (linolenic). Flax contains approximately 60% linolenic acid (LNA), and is probably the best source of Omega-3. It also contains the other essential fatty acids, 16% Linoleic (Omega-6), and 18% Oleic (Omega 9).

Flax seeds are also an excellent source of soluble lignin fiber. Flax seed lignins have a very solid amount of research demonstrating their anti-cancer effects, specifically uterine, cervical and breast cancer. Other research has demonstrated the ability of flax seed lignins to reduce blood lipids by as much as 27%. (Cunnane)

Other nutrients provided by flax seed include vitamin E, beta carotene, calcium, magnesium, manganese, potassium and high-quality protein.

A Tip For Healthier Bread...

For those of you not ready to grind your own flour and prefer to use commercial bread mixes for your bread maker.. Try adding about 1/3 cup of freshly ground flax seeds and about 1 tablespoon of honey to any commercial bread mix flavor.

This will add minerals, fiber and **lower the glycemic index** to promote balanced blood sugar levels!

What to do with freshly-ground flax seeds:

- Mix with nonfat yogurt, cottage cheese, cheese dips, etc. (the fiber helps the body rid itself of excess fat)
- Mix about 1/4 cup into meat loaf, meat balls.
- Mix about 1/3 cup into homemade breads, waffles, pancakes, muffins or other baked goods.
- Sprinkle 1-2 tablespoons (per serving) onto salads, eggs, breakfast cereal, rice or steamed vegetables.
- Add to smoothies or juice (1-2 tablespoons per serving).

Do not add flax at the stove to things like soup or cooked cereal, add it at the table instead. The fatty acids in flax seed are highly susceptible to destruction by exposure to heat, light and oxygen. This is why it is so important to use flax freshly ground. Try to prepare an amount which can be consumed right away and refrigerate or freeze any unused portions and use as soon as possible (within 1-2 days).

Flax Fruit Bars

1/3 lb. raisins
1/4 lb. dates
2 tablespoons raw honey (can add more if mixture
    does not stick together)
1/2 cup ground flax seeds
1/4 cup wheat germ
1/4 cup shredded coconut

Chop fruit in food processor. Mix in honey, flax, wheat germ and coconut. Mold mixture in a pan and refrigerate 1 hour. Cut into bars and serve. You can wrap bars in plastic wrap for a healthy snack to keep in your purse or backpack.

Note: *Dried apricots can also be used instead of the raisins and dates... I actually think I like it even better!*

Flax Almond Cookies *High in fiber*

1/2 cup whole flax seeds
1 cup kefir or buttermilk
1/2 cup butter (room temp.)
2 cups turbinado sugar (or 1 cup sugar plus 1/2 cup
    agave nectar for lower glycemic index)
2 eggs
2 tablespoon pure vanilla extract
2 cups whole wheat flour
1/2 cup freshly ground flax seeds
1 teaspoon baking soda
1 teaspoon baking powder
1/2 teaspoon sea salt
1 cup freshly chopped almonds *(or 1 teaspoon
    cardamom and 1/4 teaspoon cloves)*

Soak first two ingredients for 2 hours. In a separate bowl, cream butter and turbinado sugar until fluffy. Add one egg at a time and then add vanilla. In another bowl combine flour, ground flax, baking soda, baking powder and salt. Stir in soaked flax seeds and the butter-egg mixture and mix well. Add almonds (or spices). Form dough into balls and place on a cookie sheet 2 inches apart. Bake at 350° for 15 minutes. Remove and cool.

Flax Oatmeal Cookies
Fiber helps lower the glycemic index of these yummy treats!

- 1 cup butter
- 1 cup turbinado sugar
- 2/3 cup honey or agave nectar
- 2 eggs
- 1 teaspoon vanilla
- 1/2 cup ground flaxseed
- 1/2 teaspoon salt
- 1 teaspoon baking powder
- 1 teaspoon baking soda
- 1 teaspoon cinnamon
- 2 cups whole wheat flour
- 2 cups old fashioned rolled oats

Cream butter and sugar until light and fluffy, add eggs and vanilla and beat well. Mix together other ingredients. Stir into creamed mixture. Mix until well blended Form into 2 inch balls, place on ungreased cookie sheet about 2 1/2 inches apart. Bake at 350° for 10 minutes. Remove and cool.

Whole Wheat Flax Bread

1 cup room temperature water
3 tablespoon honey
1 tablespoon olive oil
1 1/2 cups bread flour
1 1/2 cups whole wheat flour
1 teaspoon salt
1/3 cup ground flax seeds
2 teaspoon fast rising instant yeast
Optional: 1 tablespoon sunflower seeds or 1 poppy seeds

Measure ingredients and place in bread machine pan in order recommended by the manufacturer. Select "Whole Wheat Cycle". Remove baked bread from pan. Cool on wire rack.

Banana-Date Flax Seed Bread

1 cup ground flax seeds
2/3 cup mashed banana
3/4 cup honey or 2 teaspoons stevia
2 eggs
1 cup flour (can use whole wheat)
1/2 cup flax - whole seeds
1 teaspoon baking powder
1 teaspoon baking soda
1 teaspoon salt
1 cup chopped pitted dates

Beat the banana, honey or stevia and eggs at medium speed until well blended. Combine flour, ground flax seeds, whole flax seeds, baking powder, baking soda and salt. Gradually add to mixture, beating until well-blended. Stir in dates and pour into a greased 8 x 4 inch loaf pan. Bake at 350° for 55 minutes or until a wooden pick inserted comes out clean. Cool 10 minutes in pan and remove.

Toasted Flax

Place a small amount (as much as you will consume in a day or two) of whole flax seeds on a baking sheet and bake at 325° for about 5 minutes. While you need to chew them well, this makes a great nutty, crunchy addition to salads and other dishes. They can also be eaten alone as a snack.

Apple Flax Pudding

1 tablespoon ground flax
1/4 cup apple juice
2 drops vanilla extract
Pinch of cinnamon
Optional: 1-2 tablespoon applesauce or chopped apple

Place ingredients in small bowl and stir about 20 seconds. Ready to eat. Makes 1 serving.

Veggie Flax Seed Crackers

1 lb golden flax seeds
1 carrot
1 thin slice of onion
1 thick slice of tomato
1 thick slice of red pepper
Course sea salt
Cayenne pepper - to taste

1. Juice the vegetables, add a cup of water and the salt and use it to soak the seeds (instead of plain water) for about 6 hours. Add some of the veggie pulp to the flax seeds. Add more water if necessary. Soaked flax seeds are very gelatinous and goopy, sort of like cake batter.

2. Spread out a thin layer onto cookie sheets and "bake" at 115 degrees for about 12 hours - turn over and "bake" until done.

OR with a dehydrator, dehydrate at 105° F for 12-13 hours. Then turn teflex sheets upside down and peel off. Continue dehydrating until dry. Cut or break into crackers.

Flax Crackers #1

4 cups whole flax seeds, soaked 4-6 hours
1/3 to 1/2 cup Bragg's Aminos
Juice of 2-3 lemons

Soak flax seeds for 4 to 6 hours in purified water. You will then have a gelatinous mixture, be sure to keep moist and loose for spreading. Add Bragg's and lemon juice to taste and mix well. Spread mixture as thin as possible on your dehydrator trays with a teflex sheet on top. Keep your hands wet as this will help on spreading the flax seeds (or use a spatula)

Dehydrate at 105 degrees for 5-6 hours and then flip the mixture and remove the teflex sheet. Continue dehydrating until the mixture completely dry. Approximately 5-6 hours.

Or "bake" at 115 degrees for 8-10 hours (depending on thickness of crackers) you may need to turn over for few hours to dry out bottom side.

Optional: Add garlic, onions, carrot juice, taco seasoning, Italian seasoning, chili powder, cumin in any combination. Be creative!

Flaxseed Crackers #2

1/4 cup whole flaxseed
1/4 cup ground flaxseed
1 1/2 cups flour (whole grain)
1/2 teaspoon baking powder
1/2 teaspoon sea salt
4 teaspoons butter, softened
1/2 cup milk

1. In the bowl of a stand-up mixer, put flaxseed, ground flax, flour, baking powder, salt, and butter. With paddle attachment, mix on low speed until the mixture resembles coarse meal.

2. Stir in milk, and mix until mixture forms a soft dough. (You can also mix the dough by hand.)

3. Wrap dough in plastic wrap, and chill 10 minutes.

4. Divide the dough into 4 pieces. Put a ball of dough on a lightly floured board. Roll out to a rectangle about 1/16" thick. Cut into 2 & 1/2" squares.

5. Transfer squares to an ungreased baking sheet. Repeat with remaining dough.

6. Bake in preheated 325° F oven for 20 minutes, or until crisp and golden.
VARIATION: Add 1 tablespoons powdered onion or garlic, etc.

Granola

4 cups old-fashioned thick rolled oats
1 1/2 cups wheat germ
1 cup sesame seeds
1 cup sunflower seeds or chopped nuts
   (I prefer almonds)
1/2 cup honey
1/3 cup olive oil
1/3 cup water
1/2 cup flax seed
1 cup raisins
2 teaspoons cinnamon

Combine dry ingredients into a large bowl. Heat honey, oil, and water until well blended. Add to dry ingredients and mix until all dry ingredients are moistened. Place on a cookie sheet; bake at 350° F. for 45 minutes. Stir every 15 minutes.

Low Fat Cheese Cake w/ Raspberry Lemon Topping

Mix together in large bowl:
 8 oz. lowfat cream cheese
 two tablespoons low fat or fat free sour cream
 2 large egg yolks (3 if small)
 1 teaspoon liquid stevia
 2 tablespoons lemon curd (optional)

In separate small bowl:
Beat 2 egg whites till stiff peaks form and fold into cream cheese mixture.

Pour into graham cracker crust.
Bake about 30 minutes at 350° degrees. Remove and refrigerate to cool.

Topping:
One large package of frozen raspberries
Put about 2/3 of the bag in sauce pan with about 1 table-spoon of corn starch. Slowly heat, stirring occasionally so till it boils and thickens. I added some lemon juice to bring it to the consistency I wanted. Refrigerate.

The rest of the (whole) raspberries can be placed on top when serving.
Serves about 8

Lemon Cheesecake

An easy low carb snack or dessert!

> 16 oz. cream cheese, room temperature
> 3 large eggs (divided)
> 2 teaspoons stevia
> 1 teaspoon vanilla extract
> 3 teaspoons lemon extract
> Rind from 2 medium sized lemons
> 1 cup pecans, chopped (optional)
> Pie crust of your choice (recipes on page 174)

1. Preheat the oven to 350° degrees.

Place egg yolks, cream cheese, vanilla, lemon and stevia in the large bowl of your mixer. Beat until well combined and smooth.

Beat egg whites until stiff peaks form and fold into cream cheese mixture.

Pour the cream cheese mixture into your pie crust. Place in the preheated oven and bake for 30-40 minutes, just until a knife inserted in the center comes out clean. Remove from the oven and refrigerate until ready to serve.

When serving, garnish with fresh berries, whipped cream or a mint leaf if desired.

Rhubarb Cheesecake

Same recipe as above but omit lemon and replace with cinnamon. Top with rhubarb sauce recipe at the end of this chapter.

Pumpkin Cheesecake

Very low fat, very low sugar, very yummy!

    8 ounces cream cheese (I use low fat or fat free)
    Beat until light and fluffy
    Beat in one at a time:
    2 eggs, plus one white
Stir in:
    2 cups pumpkin puree (can also use mashed
        sweet potatoes or 1/2 and 1/2)
    3 teaspoons Stevia powder
    1/8 cup real maple syrup
    1 tablespoon cinnamon
    1/2 teaspoon ginger
    1/2 teaspoon cloves
    1/4 teaspoon allspice

Pour into graham cracker pie crust

For Fluffy Cheesecake...
Beat only the 2 yolks in before the pumpkin.
Separately, beat the 3 whites and set them aside until the end and then fold them into the pumpkin cream cheese mixture. (I like this fluffy way better)

Bake at preheated oven 400° for 10 minute, reduce oven to 325° and bake for 30 more minutes. Turn off oven and leave in there for 15 or 20 more minutes. Chill before serving.
Top with whipped topping (sweeten with stevia) and drizzle top with maple syrup.

Chocolate Cheese Cake

Low glycemic and very easy to make

Mix together and pour into graham cracker crust.
- 1 8 oz. package low fat cream cheese
- 1/2 cup cocoa powder
- 2 egg yolks
- 1 teaspoon stevia (adjust to desired sweetness)
- 1 teaspoon vanilla extract
- Gently mix in 2 beaten egg whites

Optional: Mix separately and set aside:
- 1 cup sour cream
- 1 teaspoon vanilla
- Stevia liquid to taste - approx. 1/2 dropperful

Mix together and pour into graham cracker crust.
Bake about 30 minutes at 375° degrees.

If desired: Remove and smooth sour cream on top. Return to oven for another 10 minutes.

Remove and refrigerate to cool.
Serve with fresh berries.

A KEY TO HEALTHY EATING...
Moderation!

"...Hast thou found honey? Eat so much as is sufficient for thee, lest thou be filled therewith, and vomit it." Proverbs 25:16

"It is not good to eat much honey: so for men to search their own glory is not glory."
Proverbs 25:27

Fruit Tart (or Fruit Pizza)
A summertime favorite!

1 1/3 cup flour
1/2 cup finely ground almonds
1/2 teaspoon stevia
1 teaspoon lemon rind
6 tablespoons butter, very cold, cut into pieces
1 egg
1 teaspoon vanilla

Combine dry ingredients in large bowl. Cut butter into flour with pastry knife until course crumbs form. Wisk egg and vanilla together and add to flour mixture to form a dough. Shape in disk and wrap in plastic. Refrigerate for at least one hour or overnight.

Preheat oven to 350 degrees. Grease and flour baking sheet. Pat dough into 10" circle or desired shape. Pierce bottom of dough with fork all over. Bake until slightly brown. Remove from pan to cool.

Mix together:
8 ounces cream cheese
Stevia to taste - about 1 teaspoon
1/8 cup candied ginger, chopped fine

Spread upon crust. Top with about 3 cups fresh fruit of choice, sliced to small pieces. Can be all one fruit such as strawberries or a design of several colorful fruits. I often combine blueberries, strawberries and peaches, making circles or rows of each fruit.

Options:
Mix 1/8 cup fruit spread (without sugar) plus 1 teaspoon lemon juice over top of fruit as a glaze.

If using all strawberries, drizzle top with melted chocolate.

Chocolate Silk Pie

Easy, No-Bake, No-Sugar

16 oz. extra firm tofu
1/2 cup cocoa powder
2 teaspoon stevia extract (or more to taste)
Almond maple pie crust (see recipe below)
2 tablespoons slivered almonds
2 tablespoons organic chocolate chips

Mix first 3 ingredients thoroughly in food processor or blender. Spoon into pie crust. Smooth.

Optional: Sprinkle some organic chocolate chips and slivered almonds on top (Note - the chocolate chips will add some sugar.)

Finish with fresh whipped topping sweetened with stevia.

Garnish with fresh strawberries if desired.

You can also use the graham cracker crust on page 174 if you prefer.

Almond Maple Pie Crust

1 1/4 cup raw almonds, soaked in water for 8-12 hours
6-8 teaspoons real maple syrup

Drain water off of soaked almonds and dry well. Dry in oven at 100 degrees for a few hours if you have time. Place almonds in food processor and chop until they are very fine. Slowly add maple syrup, just enough to hold them together. Sprinkle into an 8 or 9 inch pie crust and gently press into the bottom and up the sides.
Serves 6

A KEY TO HEALTHY EATING...
Chocolate!!

Chocolate comes from cocoa beans which comes from a plant which God made! Scientific evidence actually shows that the consumption of dark chocolate (cocoa) can **improve** both **glucose metabolism (through improved insulin resistance and sensitivity) and blood pressure**. Cocoa is rich in flavanols, powerful antioxidant polyphenols found in plants which fight off free radical damage.

1. If you eat chocolate, only eat DARK chocolate (not milk chocolate). Dark chocolate has antioxidant properties, which can actually help to protect the body from damaging oxidative stress. But remember, just because the chocolate is dark, it does not mean it is healthy. Most cocoa is processed in ways that destroy the majority of the beneficial antioxidants.

2. Only eat chocolate if you're healthy. Most dark chocolate still contains large quantities of sugar, and eating sugar is very detrimental to the functioning of your immune system. If you are sick, the absolute last thing you want to do is eat sugar. I have included a few recipes with cocoa or dark chocolate with minimum added sugar.

3. Consume in moderation. A small bit of dark chocolate can be very satisfying if you savor each bite. However if you are constantly craving sweets, you may be experiencing a mineral imbalance (lack of chromium, i.e.). If you crave chocolate when you are stressed, upset, bored or lonely, then you could benefit from resolving these underlying emotional or spiritual root issues that are driving you to seek comfort from chocolate.

Graham Cracker Crust

1 1/2 cups graham cracker crumbs
5 tablespoons butter, melted

To make crumbs, take several graham crackers at a time and
zip them inside a large zip-lock bag and crush with a rolling
pin until you have enough crumbs to equal 1 1/2 cups. Put
the crumbs in a bowl and add the melted butter. Mix to combine. Press the crumbs evenly over the bottom and sides of
a 9 inch pie pan. Bake at 350° degrees for 8 minutes. Let
cool.

Butter Pie Crust (2-Crust Pie)

2 1/2 cups flour
1/2 teaspoon salt
1/2 cup plus 6 tablespoons cold butter, cut in pieces
2 egg yolks
4-6 tablespoons cold water

1. Sift together the flour and salt in a bowl. Add the butter
and cut in with a pastry blender or two knives until the mixture resembles coarse crumbs.

2. With a fork, stir in the egg yolks and just enough water to
bind dough together. Gather into two balls and roll each ball
out the dough on a floured surface until about 1/8 inch thick.

3. Transfer bottom crust into the pan by rolling onto the
rolling pin and unrolling it or by folding the crust twice and
unfolding it in the pie pan.

Rhubarb Crumble Pie

1 unbaked 9-inch pie shell
1 1/2 pounds rhubarb stalks (about 6 cups)
1/3 cup water
3 tablespoons whole wheat flour
About 1 and 1.2 teaspoons liquid stevia
(sometimes I also add raspberries or strawberries!)

Topping:
1/4 cup butter, room temperature
1/3 cup turbinado or brown sugar
1/3 cup whole wheat flour
1/2 cup old-fashioned rolled oats
1 teaspoon ground cinnamon

Heat oven to 350°.
Prepare pie shell or thaw a frozen pie shell.

Trim and rinse the rhubarb stalks. Slice large stalks in half
lengthwise. Slice rhubarb stalks crosswise in 1/2 to 1-inch
lengths.

Combine sliced rhubarb and water in a medium saucepan.
add 3 tablespoons flour and stevia, stirring until well blended. Stir well and bring just to a boil. Reduce heat to low.
Cover but leave the cover ajar to let steam escape and
continue simmering for about 5 minutes, or just until tender.

Spoon filling into the prepared pie shell.

With a pastry blender or fork, combine the topping ingredients until blended and crumbly.

Sprinkle over the top of the pie. Bake for 35 to 45 minutes,
until topping is browned and the filling is bubbly.

Cool before serving so it sets.

Chocolate Chip Zucchini Cake

1 1/2 cups butter softened
1/2 cup honey
1 tsp liquid stevia
1 tsp vanilla
3 eggs
2 1/2 cups All purpose flour
1/4 cup ground flax
1/4 cup unsweetened cocoa
1 tsp cinnamon
1 tsp baking soda
1/2 cup buttermilk
2 cups shredded zucchini
1/2 cup semi sweet chocolate chips
1/2 cup chopped nuts (optional)

Preheat oven to 350°
Pan Type: 13 x 9 inch glass pan or bundt
Grease pan with butter and flour.

In a large bowl, combine honey, stevia,vanilla and eggs;
beat well. Stir in buttermilk and then flour, ground flax,
cocoa, baking soda, cinnamon; blend well.

Fold in zucchini, chocolate chips and nuts.

Pour into pan.

Bake 35 to 40 minutes. until knife inserted in center comes
out clean.

Do not over bake.

Good with or without frosting!

A Tip to Sweeten Food Without Raising Blood Sugar Levels...

Stevia: The Safe, Natural and Healthy Alternative to Sugar, Splenda and Aspartame

Stevia comes from the dried leaves of the stevia plant. It is an excellent NATURAL alternative to sugar and dangerous artificial sweeteners. **It has no calories, does not raise blood sugar and has none of the side effects** or health risks of sugar, aspartame, saccharin, Splenda® and is not broken down by heat.

The natives in South America where it was originally grown, used stevia primarily as a sweetener. The indigenous tribes also used stevia to treat diabetes.

In the United States, stevia is not marketed as a sweetener, but as a dietary supplement due to federal regulations.

Stevia contains glycosides, especially stevioside, which gives stevia its sweetness. Stevioside is about 30-50 times sweeter than sugar, so you use much less. It can be used in cooking and baking in many cases just as sugar is – you simply use much less.

Stevia has beneficial effects on glucose tolerance and is therefore helpful for diabetics or someone concerned about their weight.

Stevia is available in packets, in powder form or liquid extract. One cup sugar = 1 1/2 teaspoons powdered stevia extract. Conversions are also on the package. A number of good stevia cookbooks are also available.

Lemon Buttermilk Pudding Cake with Fresh Berries

1 1/2 cups buttermilk
1/2 cup honey
1 teaspoon stevia
4 large egg yolks
1/3 cup fresh lemon juice
1/4 cup all purpose flour
1/4 cup (1/2 stick) unsalted butter, melted
1/8 teaspoon sea salt
3 large egg whites
Whipping cream
Assorted fresh berries

1. Preheat oven to 350 ° F. Butter 8x8x2-inch glass baking dish.

2. Blend buttermilk, 1/2 cup honey, egg yolks, lemon juice, flour, butter, and salt in blender until smooth. Transfer buttermilk mixture to medium bowl.

3. Using electric mixer, beat egg whites in large bowl until soft peaks form. Gradually add stevia and beat until stiff but not dry. Gently fold buttermilk mixture into whites in 3 additions (batter will be runny).

4. Pour batter into prepared dish. Place dish in roasting pan. Pour enough hot water into roasting pan to come halfway up sides of dish. Bake until entire top is evenly browned and cake moves very slightly in center but feels slightly springy to touch, about 45 minutes. Remove dish from roasting pan.

5. Cool cake completely in baking dish on rack. Refrigerate until cold, at least 3 hours and up to 6 hours. Spoon pudding cake out into shallow bowls. Pour cream around cake. Top with berries.
Servings: 6-8

Low Fat Lemon Bars

Moist, tangy lemony!

For the Base:
  1 cup whole wheat flour
  1/4 cup turbinado or brown sugar
  1/2 cup rolled oats
  3 tbsp butter

For the Topping:
  2 eggs
  1/2 cup turbinado sugar
  1 teaspoon liquid stevia
  3 tbsp whole wheat flour
  1/4 tsp baking powder
  Pinch of sea salt
  Juice and zest of 2 large lemons
  2 additional tablespoons lemon juice concentrate

Preheat oven to 350 degrees.
Coat an 8-inch square baking glass pan with butter.

Combine flour, oats and sugar in a medium bowl. Using a pastry blender, add butter and blend until the mixture is crumbly.

Press crumbs into the bottom of the baking pan. Bake for 10 minutes until edges are golden.

Meanwhile, whisk eggs. Add sugar, stevia and beat until creamy. Add flour, baking powder, salt and lemon; whisk until smooth.

Pour lemon mixture over pre-baked base. Bake for 20-25 minutes, or until center is set.

Cool on wire rack to cool completely.

Pumpkin-Nut Loaf

Pumpkins are the giants of the squash family, nutritionally and by size. Pumpkin is loaded with the anti-aging antioxidant beta carotene and fiber. Serve this pumpkin-nut loaf plain or with apple butter for dessert. For lunch, toast and top with a mild-flavored cheese.

1 1/2 cups whole wheat flour
1/2 cup real maple syrup
1 teaspoon stevia
1 teaspoon baking powder
1 teaspoon cinnamon and nutmeg
3/4 teaspoon sea salt
1 1/2 cups cooked pumpkin puree
1/4 cup extra-light olive oil
2 whole eggs
1 egg white
1/2 cup grated carrot
1/4 cup ground flax seeds
1/4 cup pine nuts
1/4 cup chopped pistachio nuts
(instead of nuts, you could substitute raisins)

1. Preheat the oven to 350°F. Spread butter or olive oil inside a 9 x 5-inch loaf pan.

2. In a large bowl, blend the flour with the sugar, baking powder, cinnamon, nutmeg and salt. Add the pumpkin, oil, whole egg, egg whites, carrot, pine nuts, and pistachios, and stir until evenly blended.

3. Transfer the batter to the loaf pan and spread evenly. Bake about 45 minutes, or until a toothpick inserted in the center comes out dry. Cool for 20 minutes in the pan, then invert onto a rack to cool completely. Slice and serve.

Servings: 12

Chocolate Chocolate Chip Cookies

2 1/4 cups multi-grain flour (I use wheat, barley and
    rye)
1/2 cup ground flax seeds
1/2 cup cocoa powder
1 teaspoon baking soda
1 teaspoon sea salt
1 cup (2 sticks) butter, softened
3/4 cup honey
1/2 cup packed brown sugar
1 teaspoon vanilla extract
2 large eggs
1 12-oz. pkg.semi-sweet chocolate chips
1 cup chopped almonds (OR chopped dried cherries)

1. Preheat oven to 375° F.

2. Combine flour, flax, cocoa, baking soda and sea salt in small bowl.

3. Beat butter, honey, brown sugar and vanilla extract in large mixer bowl until creamy. Add eggs, one at a time, beating well after each addition.

4. Gradually mix in flour mixture.

5. Stir in morsels and nuts. Drop by rounded tablespoon onto ungreased baking sheets.

6. Bake for 9 to 11 minutes or until golden brown. Cool on baking sheets for 2 minutes; remove to wire racks to cool completely.

Dark Chocolate Orange Tart
Low Sugar

(With thanks to Cheryl Orluck and "The Naked Chef")

Pastry Crust (makes enough for 1 large 10 inch crust)
  2 cups whole wheat flour
  1/3 cup room temperature organic butter (about 3/4 stick)
  1/3 cup confectioners sugar
  2 teaspoons powdered stevia
  pinch of sea salt
  1 tablespoon vanilla extract
  1 tablespoon zest of an orange
  3 egg yolks
  2 tablespoons cold milk or water

1. Cream together butter and sugar and salt. Rub in flour, zest and vanilla until it looks like course bread crumbs. Add milk or water enough to form a ball, don't overwork.

2. Push into pan. Freeze for one hour.

3. Bake at 350° for 15 minutes - no filling. Remove. Mix together one egg and brush over top of crust.

4. Lower oven temp to 325° degrees.

Filling
  9 oz. ricotta cheese
  9 oz. mascarpone or cream cheese
  2 tablespoons stevia powder (add a bit of honey if you want it sweeter)
  Remaining zest of 3 oranges
  Vanilla extract, 1 teaspoon
  1 egg yolk
  3 egg whites, beat until stiff
  3.5 ounce best-quality bittersweet chocolate, roughly chopped

208

5. Mix cheese, egg yolk and stevia until smooth. Add zest and other ingredients. Fold in egg whites.

6. Pour into tart. Top with chocolate pieces.

7. Bake for 40 minutes.

Serve room temperature or chilled with fresh whipped topping: Beat heavy cream until stiff, add vanilla extract and stevia.

Apple Oat Bars *(from Chet Day)*

   2 cups thick rolled oats
   1 cup raisins or chopped dates
   1 or more cups unsweetened coconut (optional)
   2 small apples, grated, peeling and all!
   2 cups milk
   1/2 cup slivered almonds
   1 teaspoon cinnamon or apple pie spices

1. In an 8" x 8" baking dish, sprinkle 1/3 of the oats on the bottom of the dish.

2. Layer 1/2 of the raisins or dates, 1/2 of the coconut, another 1/3 of the oats, all of the apples, and top with spices.

3. Pour on 1/2 of the milk. Continue by adding the rest of the raisins, oats and coconut, and spices. Top with the almonds and sprinkle with cinnamon. Pour on the rest of the milk. Bake at 350° for 30 minutes. Let cool, cut into bars.

Dr. Beth's Carrot Cake

Combine and set aside to soak for several hours or overnight:
- 4 cups shredded carrots
- 1/2 cup finely chopped dried apricots
- 1/4 cup frozen orange juice concentrate

Beat the next 4 ingredients together. Then add 1 egg at a time. Add remaining ingredients and beat until light in color.
- 3/4 cup melted butter
- 1/4 cup brown sugar
- 3/4 cup honey
- 2 teaspoons stevia powder
- 4 eggs, room temperature
- 3 teaspoons vanilla extract
- grated rind of 1 lemon

Beat first 4 ingredients together. Then add 1 egg at a time. Add remaining ingredients and beat until light in color.

Sift together twice:
- 3 3/4 cups whole wheat flour
- 1/3 cup finely ground flax seeds
- 3/4 teaspoon sea salt
- 1/2 teaspoon baking soda
- 3 1/2 teaspoons baking powder
- 1 teaspoon ground allspice
- 3 teaspoons cinnamon
- 1/2 teaspoon cloves

Add flour mixture and grated carrots alternately to butter mixture. (Save a small amount of the carrots to sprinkle on top of frosted cake)Start and end with flour. mix gently, do not over beat or it will toughen the cake.

Pour into buttered 8 x 10 pan, 2 loaf pans or 2-3 rounds for stacking. Bake at 350 degrees for about an hour, less for rounds. It's best to do toothpick test for doneness.

Frosting:

    16 ounces of organic cream cheese
    2 teaspoons of liquid stevia extract
    2 teaspoons vanilla
    1/3 cup slivered almonds
    1/4 cup shredded carrots

Mix together cream cheese, stevia and vanilla with hand mixer and spread on top of cake. Sprinkle almonds and carrots on top to decorate.

Apricot Pudding Cake

Vitamin-A-rich apricots, cheese and stevia make this a tangy, tasty low glycemic desert

    1/2 cup chopped dried apricots
    1 cup orange juice
    1 cup ricotta cheese
    4 oz. cream cheese
    3 tablespoons honey
    1 teaspoon stevia
    3/4 cup cornmeal
    1/3 cup whole wheat flour
    1/4 teaspoon grated nutmeg
    1/4 cup slivered almonds

1. Preheat oven to 300°F. Soak apricots in 1/2 cup water in small bowl 15 minutes. Drain and discard water. Pat apricots dry with paper towels; set aside.

2. Combine orange juice, ricotta cheese and honey in medium bowl. Mix on medium speed of electric mixer 5 minutes or until smooth. Combine stevia, cornmeal, flour and nutmeg in small bowl. Gradually add flour mixture to orange juice mixture; blend well. Slowly stir in apricots.

3. Pour batter into buttered spring form pan. Sprinkle with almonds. Bake 60 to 70 minutes or until center is firm and cake is golden brown. Serve warm.

A KEY TO HEALTHY BLOOD SUGAR LEVELS...
Cinnamon!!

Researchers tell us that cinnamon (which contains some-thing they call MHCP) makes fat cells much more responsive to insulin and prevents the formation of dam-aging oxygen radicals. This substance also reduces blood pressure in animals with high pressure readings.

This is significant because other studies have shown that antioxidant supplements can reduce or slow the progres-sion of various complications of diabetes.

a 2004 Pakistan study found that 1-6 grams of cinna-mon, daily for 40 days, reduces fasting blood glucose by 18-29%, triglycerides by 23-30%, LDL-cholesterol by 7-27%, and total cholesterol by 12-26%. There was no 'dose-effect'; thus it's not known if less than 1 gram a day would be equally beneficial. The changes persisted, largely, for 20 days after the patients had stopped taking extra cinnamon.

A comment by one of the authors of this report, "I don't know of anything else that can change glucose, triglyc-erides and cholesterol levels nearly so much".

• Cinnamon improves glucose and lipids of people with type 2 dia-betes. A. Kahn, M. Safdar, MM. Ali Kahn, et al., Diabetes Care, 2003, vol. 26, pp. 3215--3218

The best (most effective) way to use cinnamon is to buy sticks of cinnamon, grind it and add it to bread, desserts, rice and cereal recipes and as a tea with stevia after a meal.

Cinnamon Raisin Rice Pudding

Simmer on stove for 15-20 minutes until water is soaked up:
    1 1/2 cups organic raisins
    2 teaspoons cinnamon
    1 cup water

Simmer on stove (about 40 minutes) until rice is cooked:
    2 cups brown or wild rice
    4 cups milk
    1-2 cinnamon sticks

Add:1/2 cup 1/2 and 1/2
    Stevia to taste
    Raisins

Simmer for another 10 minutes. Serve warm in bowl.

Chocolate Chestnut Mousse

    2 pounds of chestnuts, scored, roasted, then peeled
    1 teaspoon stevia
    6 tablespoons of cocoa (dark chocolate)
    4 tablespoons of amaretto (optional - provides sugar)
    16 ounces heavy whipping cream

Put chestnuts in food processor and chop until fine. Add stevia, cocoa and amaretto. Process until smooth and well mixed.

Beat heavy cream until stiff. Fold into chestnut puree. Divide among desert glasses. Chill until set-up.

Serve with a dollop of whipped cream and chocolate shavings. Serves 10.

NOTE: Mousse can also be used as filling for cream puffs or between multiple very thin layers of cake and then drizzled with raspberry puree.

Fruit Dip with Fresh Fruit
Fast and so simple!

> 1/2 cup cream cheese (recipe for homemade on page
>   218)
> 1/3 cup ricotta cheese
> 4-6 drops stevia (to taste)
> 1/2 teaspoon vanilla
> 1/2 teaspoon cinnamon

Mix and serve with fresh fruit - sliced apple, pear, strawberries or other berries, etc.

Stewed Rhubarb

> 6 cups chopped rhubarb
> About 1 cup water

Simmer on stovetop for 45 minutes to 1 hour until rhubarb is very soft. Then add:
> 2 teaspoons cinnamon
> Stevia to taste, I use about 1 teaspoon of the liquid

Serve with yogurt, cream or fruit dip.

Salsa
I like it HOT - but you can make it to your own taste!

Place ingredients in food processor and chop:
  1 to 2 large tomatoes
  1 small onion
  3 cloves garlic
  1/2 red bell pepper
  1 jalapeno pepper
  2-3 serrano peppers (depending how hot you like it)
  1/2 to 1 habanera pepper *(if* you can tolerate the heat!)
  1/2 bunch fresh cilantro
  1/2 teaspoon honey
  2-3 tablespoons lime juice
  3 tablespoons tomato paste
  1 teaspoon red pepper flakes
  1 teaspoon cumin
  dash of sea salt

Spicy Black Bean Dip

  2 cups cooked black beans
  1/2 cup chopped onion
  1 sliced roasted red bell pepper (remove skin)
  2-3 tablespoons salsa
  1 teaspoon cajun seasoning
  Add to personal preference: cayenne, garlic, etc.

Place items in food processor and blend until smooth.
Serve with vegetables, non-hydrogenated oil corn chips or
tortillas.

Lentil Pate

1 1/2 cups cooked pinto beans or 1 15 oz. can
1 cup cooked lentils-cooked in vegetable or meat stock
1/2 cup chopped onions
3 tablespoons lemon juice
2 cloves garlic, minced
1/2 teaspoon red pepper

Place items in food processor and blend until smooth. Spoon into crock or serving dish. It is best to refrigerate overnight to blend favors. Serve as a dip for vegetables or as a spread for crackers. Top with chopped green onion if desired.

Hummus

Put in processor:

3+ cups cooked garbanzo beans (save some of the cooking water)
1 large clove garlic roasted (cut off top - put in bed of tin foil drizzle with olive oil, bake at 350 degrees for 45 minutes)
Pinch of cayenne pepper
Splash of Bragg's aminos or soy sauce
Sea salt to taste
Lemon juice
Heaping tablespoon of Tahini or sesame butter
1/4 cup extra virgin olive oil

Save some of the water from cooking beans to add to processor when mixing.
Drizzle in some olive oil while mixing to bring to desired consistency. (about 1/4 cup or less)
If too thick add some of the cooking water.
Taste and add more seasoning if needed.

Serve with veggies, crackers or use it to make a sandwich.
Makes a great lunch to take to work!
NOTE: This recipe can also be made with any white bean, navy or butter bean (lima) for example.

White Cheese Jalapeno Dip

2 tablespoons butter
1/2 white onion, chopped
1 cup jalapenos chopped, red and green
1 tablespoon whole wheat flour
1/2 cup 1/2 and 1/2 or milk
2 tablespoons Tabasco
1/2 teaspoon sea salt
1/2 teaspoon cayenne pepper... or to taste.
1 pound fontina cheese, grated
1/2 cup other white cheese - mozzarella, etc.

Granola

3 tablespoons butter, melted in 9x13 pan in oven
2 tablespoons apple or orange juice
2 teaspoons stevia powder
2 tablespoons real maple syrup
2 cups thick rolled oats
1/3 cup sunflower seeds
1/3 cup slivered almonds
1/2 cup wheat germ
1/2 cup raisins or chopped dried apple
2 teaspoons cinnamon

Heat oven to 350. When butter is melted, remove from oven and add maple syrup and juice and stir. Add other ingredients except last 3. Bake for 15 minutes, remove and stir in last 3 ingredients and bake about 10 minutes.

Trail Mix

Combine and mix together:
- 3/4 cup golden or red raisins
- 1/4 cup dried cherries, cranberries, apples, pineapple
  other dried fruit (chopped if necessary)
- 1/2 cup raw almonds and raw cashews
- 1/2 cup raw sunflower seeds, peanuts or other nuts

Cream Cheese (Homemade)

Cheese cloth
1 quart plain yogurt (preferably homemade)

Place cheese cloth over a large glass bowl or pan. Secure with a rubber band. Create a slight indentation into the cheese cloth to form a "bowl." Pour the yogurt into the "bowl" and let the whey drip through the cheese cloth. The remaining on top is your cream cheese! This will take 4-8 hours. Be sure to store the whey in a glass jar in the fridge for other valuable uses. Yields about 8 ounces

Yogurt (Homemade) *So easy to make!*

1/2 cup good quality organic yogurt
1 quart unhomogenized whole milk

Gently warm milk on stove (no higher than 180 degrees), let cool to 110 and stir in the 1/2 cup yogurt. Warm oven to about 110. Turn off the oven and turn on the light to keep the oven warm. Pour into a glass or stainless steel container, cover and place in oven for about 12 hours. Try not to open the door to keep the heat in. Remove and refrigerate.

Whipped Cream

Whip with wisk or electric mixer:
    1/2 cup heavy whipping cream
    Add: 1 teaspoon real vanilla extract
    1 teaspoon stevia liquid extract (more if you like)

Add to desserts, fruit salad, etc.

THE TRUTH...

Now the Spirit speaketh expressly, that in the latter times some shall depart from the faith, giving heed to seducing spirits, and doctrines of devils; Speaking lies in hypocrisy; having their conscience seared with a hot iron; Forbidding to marry, and commanding to abstain from foods, which God hath created to be received with thanksgiving of them which believe and know the truth.

1 Timothy 4:1-3

Hot Harvest Cider
This low-glycemic drink should not raise your blood sugar!

2 quarts apple cider
1/4 cup lemon juice
1 teaspoon liquid stevia extract
1/2 teaspoon ground allspice
1/2 teaspoon ground nutmeg
12 whole cloves
2 cinnamon sticks

Place the first five ingredients in a large kettle. Bring to a simmer. Place the cloves and cinnamon stick in a cheesecloth bag and drop into the pot. Simmer about 10 minutes. Ladle into mugs to serve. Serves about 10.

Fresh Lemonade

1 cup fresh lemon juice (from about 5 lemons)
1 teaspoon Liquid Stevia (according to taste)
6-7 cups water

Place the lemon juice, stevia and water in a 2 quart glass jar. Stir briefly to dissolve the stevia. Refrigerate. Adjust the amount of lemon juice and stevia as desired. Serve over ice.

Almond Milk

1 1/2 cups of raw almonds, soaked in water overnight
4 cups of filtered or spring water
3-5 dates (optional) could also sweeten with stevia

Blend 1 1/2 cups of raw almonds (and dates) that have been soaked overnight in 4 cups of water. Strain to remove granules. The result is a delicious, creamy milk that is free of harmful vegetable oil, concentrated sweeteners, carnageenen, and the problems associated with cow's milk and soy.

GLYCEMIC INDEX

The glycemic index is a rating system indicating how different foods affect the rise in blood sugar. Foods that have the most dramatic affect on blood sugar are rated higher. Sugar, which is rated 100, has the most dramatic effect on blood sugar levels, and therefore, receives the highest score. The higher a glycemic index food number is, the faster it raises your blood sugar level.

Eat more low glycemic index foods that promote a slow, moderate rise in blood sugar and insulin after eating them. This helps keep hunger in check and encourages the body to dissolve body fat by converting it into energy. These foods allow you to consume more calories without gaining weight. They actually increase your metabolic rate.

Avoid high glycemic index foods. These cause sudden, unstable swings in blood sugar, first with rapid, very high sugar and insulin surges, followed by a crash of sugar to excessively low levels. These foods increase your cravings for simple carbohydrates, sweets, etc., causing overeating.

• Increase foods high in soluble fiber such as flax, lentils and beans, which have a lower glycemic response.

• Fat lowers a glycemic rating of a food because it slows absorption of the sugars. Even though they are high in sugar, regular ice cream and yogurt, have a lower glycemic rate because of their high fat content. Reduced fat and non-fat varieties have a higher glycemic index rate.

• Protein lowers the glycemic index of a food when combined with it. For example, eating some nuts or cheese with an orange or banana results in a lesser impact on blood sugar compared to just eating fruit alone. It is a very good idea to eat some protein every time you eat to promote balanced blood sugar levels.

For example: A breakfast containing instant cereal with orange juice and skim milk will send your blood sugar sky rocketing. And then... you will be even **more** hungry one hour after eating. Examples of blood-sugar "friendly" breakfasts include:

1. **Fruit smoothie with Greek yogurt and ground flax seeds**

2. **Ezekiel bread, toasted, with butter or cream cheese and two soft boiled eggs.**

3. **1/2 cup raw almonds and 1 orange**

4. **Poached eggs over steamed spinach**

• Juiced and pureed fruits and vegetables have a higher glycemic rating than whole fruits or vegetables.

• Generally, the longer you cook foods that are primarily carbohydrates (like potatoes or vegetables), the more simple the sugars become and the higher the glycemic rating.

• The more you alter a food (and especially through commercial processing), the higher the glycemic index rating becomes. Mashed potatoes have a higher rate than whole potatoes. Corn bread has a higher glycemic index than steamed corn on the cob.

Applesauce has a higher rating than raw apples. Rice flour has a higher rate than whole rice

• The more intact (natural) the food is, the healthier your insulin response will be after eating it.

Keep in mind that NATURAL higher glycemic foods like pineapple, watermelon or carrots can be enjoyed in moderation. It is best however, to not eat them alone, but combine them with yogurt, cottage cheese or other low glycemic food to balance the blood sugar response.

Normally, people do not eat a baked potato *alone* - which would promote a high blood sugar response. However, adding butter, sour cream or ricotta cheese lowers the body's response as well the chicken or steak and even green salad it is usually eaten with. These foods together form a meal of a moderate or even healthy glycemic response.

High Glycemic Index Foods

AVOID these foods to minimize insulin increases!

Sugar, corn syrup 100
Dates 100
Frozen tofu desserts 100
Hard liquor 95
Rice (instant) 91
Carrot juice 90
Puffed rice cereal 90
Rice Chex cereal 89
Honey (processed) 87
Cakes and most desserts 70-87
Corn flakes cereal 84
Potatoes (russet-baked, not eating skin) 84
Potatoes (instant) 84
Pretzels 83
Rice Krispies cereal 82
Rice cakes 82
Jelly beans 80
Angel food cake 77
Vanilla wafers 77
Stuffing 77
Waffles, pancakes 77
Watermelon 72-76
Carrots 65-76
White bread 75
French fries 75
Cheerios cereal 75
Corn bran cereal 75
Saltine crackers, water crackers 75
Potatoes (boiled) 74
Bran Flakes cereal 74
Banana (over-ripe) 74
Graham crackers 74

Raisin Bran cereal 73
Potatoes (mashed) 73
Beer 73
Bagel (plain) 72
Whole wheat bread 72
Millet 71
Cream of wheat cereal 71
Grape-Nuts cereal 71
Corn Chips 71-77
Rice (regular, white) 70
Lifesavers candy (5 - mint) 70
Corn tortilla 70
English muffin 70
Tapioca 70
Potato chips 70
Shredded Wheat cereal 69
Corn meal 68
Taco Shells 68
Wheat Thins crackers 68
Brown rice 68
Baked beans (canned) 68
Gnocchi (potato pasta) 67
Life cereal 66
Oatmeal (quick cooking) 66
Pineapple 66
Banana 60-65
Raisins 65
Melons 65
Couscous 65
Rye bread (regular) 64
Ice cream (regular; reduced fat varieties would
    have a higher rating) 64
Cola beverage 64
Figs, dried (3) 61
Orange juice 60
Popcorn 60
Pasta (regular white, refined) 60
Bran muffin 60

Low Glycemic Index Foods

Eat More of these foods to maintain healthy glucose levels!

Celery, lettuce 0
Green vegetables, eggplant, onions, garlic, cauliflower, sprouts, radishes, etc. (fresh is lower than cooked) 0-25
Eggs 10
Peanuts 10
Agave nectar (1 tablespoon) used as a natural sweetener .11
Most meats and fish (unprocessed) 12
Yogurt (plain, unsweetened) 14
Soybeans 18
Fructose (fruit sugar) 22
Cherries 22
Dark chocolate (70% cocoa) .22
Plums 25
Grapefruit 25
Lentils (red) 25
Barley (pearled) 25
Milk (regular) 27
Kidney beans 27
Milk (whole) 27
Lentils (green) 29
Apricots, dried 30
Black beans 30
Kidney beans 30
Butter beans 31
Cottage Cheese 31
Milk (skim) 32
Split peas 32
Strawberries, raspberries, blackberries (fresh) 32
Flax seeds 32
Chickpeas (garbanzo beans) .33
Vermicelli pasta 35
Pears 36
Tomatoes 38
Pinto beans 39
Navy beans 38

Yogurt (sweetened, regular fat) 38-45
Apples 30-38
Peaches 30-40
Spaghetti pasta (longer length may slow-down effects) 40
Peanut butter (no sugar added) 40
Blueberries (fresh) 40
Apple juice 41
Oats (steel cut) 42
Black-eyed peas 42
Kidney beans (canned) 42
Chickpeas (canned) 42
Grapes 45
Soy milk 43
Banana (under-ripe) 43
Oranges 40-44
Red wine 44
All Bran cereal 44
Whole wheat pasta 45
Rice, parboiled 47
Bulgur (whole grain wheat) .47
Wild rice 48
Yams 48
Nekutli Agave Nectar 48
Pumpernickel bread 49
Grapefruit juice 49
Rye bread (whole grain) 50
Oatmeal (regular, old fashioned) 50
Green Peas (fresh or frozen) 51
Kiwi 52
Sourdough bread 52
Buckwheat (Kasha) 54
Sweet potatoes 54
Pasta (protein enriched) 55
Oat bran cereal 55
Sweet corn 55-60
Mango 55
Potatoes (new, boiled) 57
Honey (raw) 58
Pita bread 58
Potatoes, red skinned (eat skins) 58
Beets 59

228

About The Author...

Beth M. Ley, Ph.D., has been a science writer specializing in health and nutrition since 1988 and has written many health-related books, including the best sellers, ***DHEA: Unlocking the Secrets to the Fountain of Youth*** and ***MSM: On Our Way Back to Health With Sulfur***. She wrote her own undergraduate degree program and graduated in Scientific and Technical Writing from North Dakota State University in 1987 (combination of Zoology and Journalism). Dr. Beth has her masters (1998) and doctoral degrees (1999) in Nutrition.

Dr. Beth does Biblical-based nutrition and wellness counseling in the Twin Cities area and also on line (www.blpublications.com). She speaks on Biblical nutrition, health and Divine healing locally and nationwide.

Dr. Beth currently lives in the Minneapolis area with her husband Michael Knotts. Together they produce "Recipes For Life with Dr. Beth" seen on local cable TV throughout MN and nationwide through Sky Angel and Direct TV.

Memberships: American Academy of Anti-aging, New York Academy of Sciences, Oxygen Society and Resurrection Apostolic International Network (RAIN), and Omega Team.

BOOKS FROM BL PUBLICATIONS

Order Toll Free 1-877-BOOKS11
Also visit us at www.blpublications.com

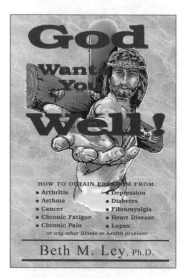

240 pages, $14.95
ISBN: 1-890766-19-4

50 pages, $5.95
ISBN: 1-890766-28-3

48 pages, $5.95
ISBN: 0-890766-24-0

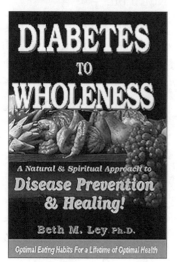

120 pages, $9.95
ISBN: 0-890766-23-2

58 pages, $5.95

ISBN: 0-962470-9-0

48 pages, $4.95

ISBN: 0-890766-00-3

220 pages, $15.95
ISBN: 0-890766-22-4

40 pages, $4.95
ISBN: 0-9642701-5-1

Orders call toll free: 1-877-BOOKS11
Or visit: www.blpublications.com